Scholastic **Theme Centre** for early years

People who help us

Lorraine Gale

Published by:
Scholastic Ltd,
Villiers House,
Clarendon Avenue,
Leamington Spa,
Warwickshire CV32 5PR

Visit our website at
www.scholastic.co.uk

Printed by Bell & Bain
Ltd, Glasgow

© 2002 Scholastic Ltd
Text © Lorraine Gale 2002
1234567890 2345678901

SERIES
CONSULTANT
Lesley Clark

AUTHOR
Lorraine Gale

EDITOR
Jayne Lacny

ASSISTANT EDITOR
Saveria Mezzana

SERIES DESIGNERS
Joy Monkhouse and
Clare Brewer

DESIGNER
Clare Brewer

ILLUSTRATIONS
Cathy Hughes

British Library Cataloguing-in-Publication Data
A catalogue record for this book is available from the British Library.

ISBN 0 439 98357 6

Books in this Centre:
The Gotcha Smile by Rita Phillips Mitchell and Alex Ayliffe (Orchard Books)
Freddie Visits the Doctor by Nicola Smee (Little Orchard)
What Would We Do Without Missus Mac? by Gus Clarke (Andersen Press)
People Who Help by Karen Bryant-Mole (Heinemann)
In the City by Sally Hobson (Walker Books)
Flashing Fire Engines by Tony Mitton and Ant Parker (Kingfisher)

Acknowledgements:
The publishers gratefully acknowledge permission to reproduce the
following copyright material:
Johanne Levy for the use of 'We are friends all dancing', 'Be my friend',
'Who wears a hard hat?' and 'The firefighter' by Johanne Levy © 2002,
Johanne Levy, all previously unpublished.
Brenda Williams for the use of 'Your pink pill', 'Poor little Jenny' and
'I've got a cold!' by Brenda Williams © 2002, Brenda Williams, all
previously unpublished.
Qualifications and Curriculum Authority for the use of extracts
from the QCA/DfEE document *Curriculum Guidance for the Foundation
Stage* © 2000, Qualifications and Curriculum Authority.

Every effort has been made to trace copyright holders and the publishers
apologize for any inadvertent omissions.

People who help us

Introduction

 Introduction

People Who Help Us is part of the *Theme Centre for Early Years* series, which is written for all professional childcare practitioners who work with three- to five-year-olds, including nursery nurses, nursery and Reception teachers, playgroup leaders and day nursery staff. The series aims to provide a collection of books, activities, stories, rhymes, songs and ideas based upon a number of specific themes for use with a thematic approach to planning.

People who help us

'People who help us' is a popular early years theme and a wonderful opportunity for children to think about the world in which they live and the variety of people that they see in their daily lives. Most young children have had experience of being helped by their family, a doctor or a shop assistant. Work on 'People who help us' can encourage them to think of a whole range of people who help them. These might include those helpers closest to them, such as their family, as well as those in high-profile jobs, such as firefighters. It can also incorporate people who help to keep them healthy, such as the chemist, or those who help to make the environment a better place to live, such as the gardener. The theme can also be used to encourage children to think about the needs of other people and the effects of their actions towards others, especially in role-play situations.

The Theme Centre Box

■ The *Theme Centre* for *People Who Help Us* contains six children's books, both story-books and information books, on the theme of 'People who help us', written for children aged three to five by well-known authors and illustrators.
■ The 128-page activity book devotes one chapter to each of the books and contains activities, ideas, photocopiable sheets, stories, rhymes and songs on the theme, for use by voluntary staff and trained teachers.
■ There are two A2 posters showing images linked to the theme. One depicts different members of the family and friends, and the other shows people who help us in the community, such as a teacher and a nurse.

How to use the Centre

Each of the children's books in the Centre has been chosen for its appeal to the early years age range. All the books have 'People who help us' as their main theme, and each will help the children to develop further their knowledge and understanding about the different types of people who help them, the jobs that they do, the tools that they need and where they can be found.

■ *The Gotcha Smile* by Rita Phillips Mitchell and Alex Ayliffe (Orchard Books) explores how our families can give help and support to us when we need it. It also shows some of the ways in which we can make or break friendships.

■ *Freddie Visits the Doctor* by Nicola Smee (Little Orchard) introduces children to the people who help to keep us healthy, such as our family, doctor and chemist.

■ *What Would We Do Without Missus Mac?* by Gus Clarke (Andersen Press) shows that there are many ways in which people can be helped. The book can be used as a stimulus to encourage children to discuss how they feel about the people who help them.

■ *People Who Help* by Karen Bryant-Mole (Heinemann) provides information about a variety of people who help, and shows them helping others, wearing uniforms and using the tools of their jobs. The book has photographs of both adults helping others and children dressed up as people who help us, so the reader can pretend to be some of these people too.

■ *In the City* by Sally Hobson (Walker Books) introduces children to the people who help to build our environment and improve the area where we live.

■ *Flashing Fire Engines* by Tony Mitton and Ant Parker (Kingfisher) develops children's understanding of the nature of the work of a fire crew and shows them the importance of teamwork.

Planning

Before starting any of the activities, read through the relevant book with the children. Every chapter can be used as a stand-alone mini topic, as it contains a range of activities from all the curriculum areas of the Foundation Stage. Alternatively, the chapters can be used in conjunction with one another to provide a larger theme. They do not have to be followed in the same sequence as they appear in the book. You can also just select single activities to support the children's learning in other topics.

Each chapter contains activities covering each of the Areas of Learning, and every activity has a learning objective linked to the Early Learning Goals. Ideas to extend the children's learning are included at the end of each activity. Additional resources are in the form of photocopiable sheets (stories, rhymes, songs, activities and games) and learning can be further developed through the role-play activity at the end of each chapter. The book also has a list of resources to supplement the theme, such as children's books and equipment.

Links to the Early Learning Goals

The practical activities in each book cover all the Areas of Learning:
■ Communication, language and literacy
■ Mathematical development
■ Personal, social and emotional development
■ Knowledge and understanding of the world

■ Physical development
■ Creative development.

As well as offering learning objectives aimed at the Early Learning Goals, the Communication, language and literacy and Mathematical development activities also include separate, but linked, objectives taken from the National Literacy Strategy and the National Numeracy Strategy respectively.

The activities

The activities are designed to be used by both professional and voluntary childcare practitioners in formal and informal settings, and have each been written in the same easy-to-follow format. The activities can either be used together or individually to support work for other themes. However, for each activity, you will need the relevant children's book.

Every activity details the resources needed, step-by-step instructions on how to carry out the activity, ways to support or extend the children's work, further ideas to develop the children's thinking, and ideas to involve parents and carers at home in their children's learning. The group sizes are the recommended number of children that can try an activity with an adult. These are guidelines only, and should be adapted to suitable individual needs and situations.

Using the posters

The two posters are used to support some of the activities and further ideas in the activity book. They are ideal display materials to introduce a topic, stimulate discussion or develop the children's thinking about one aspect of the theme. The poster depicting members of the family and friends will allow the children to talk about their own families and friends. The poster that shows people who help us in the community will prompt the children to discuss the ways in which these and other people provide care and safety, and generally help to improve our lives.

The photocopiable sheets

Included in the activity book are 23 pages which may be photocopied to support the activities. There is a collection of one story, two poems and four songs, which can lead to discussions about shop assistants, doctors, firefighters and friends. There are also games that the children will delight in playing, such as 'Lotto'. With the other photocopiable sheets, the children will learn more about story sequencing, counting, letter recognition and our senses.

Links to other themes

Although the activities in this Centre are tailored to support the theme of 'People who help us', many of the activities can be linked to other themes. Here are some suggestions:
■ Families and friends can be included in themes on 'Ourselves', 'Families', 'Celebrations' and 'Starting school'.
■ Doctors are closely linked to a topic on 'Keeping healthy'.
■ Gardeners would fit into a topic on 'Growth'.
■ Builders can be included in themes on 'Houses' and 'Our local area'.

Links with home

Parents and carers have a vital part to play in their children's education. It is important to foster good relationships with them and to help them feel involved in their children's development and learning. Each activity suggests ideas that they could try at home with their children. These are only suggestions and you may think of further ideas for strengthening home links while you use the activities.

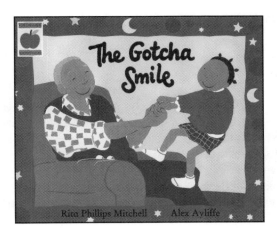

Chapter 1

The Gotcha Smile

Clarine starts a new school and wants to make friends. When she finds it hard, she turns to her family. Her parents offer advice, but her grandfather's suggestion of a friendly smile is the best. This book shows how families can positively help children with everyday problems, and it enables children to think about the actions that help to make or break friendships.

Using the book

Smiles and letter recognition begin the Communication, language and literacy section. Then the children have the opportunity to talk about their memories of the day that they first met the rest of the group in your setting. They also each write down the name of one of their friends and the reasons why they like them.

In the Mathematical development activities, the children compare Grandpa's large hand with Clarine's small hand, then compare their own hands. Inspired by the story, the children share cherries with their friends, and a new song on the theme of friendship is used to develop their understanding of number sequences.

In the Personal, social and emotional activities, the children discuss some of the things that they have done to help others, and a heart-shaped game prompts them to think about how they can make or break friendships.

In the Knowledge and understanding of the world activities, the children learn about past events in their friends' lives as they talk about how their families have helped them. They also have the opportunity to each make a ball for a friend.

The Physical development activities invite the children to work co-operatively with balls and hoops, and to play a friend-finding game.

In Creative development, the children use their imagination to paint a life-size picture of a friend. Following on from the Personal, social and emotional activities, they create a dance, based on the actions that they use to show people that they like them.

In the role-play activity, the children pretend that they are starting a new school.

Communication, language and literacy

Smile!

Learning objective
To link sounds to letters, naming and sounding the letters of the alphabet.

National Literacy Strategy
To sound and name each letter of the alphabet in lower and upper case.

Group size
Four or more children.

What you need
26 sheets of white A4 card; scissors; marker pen.

What to do
Cut two large discs from each sheet of card. Using every letter from both the upper-case and lower-case alphabets, write one letter in the centre of each circle.

Read the book and ask the children to smile. Show them the disc with the 'u' on it. Explain that it is the letter 'u' and that it looks a bit like a smile. Sit the children in a circle, facing towards the middle. Give each child one of the card discs. Make sure that one of the children is given the letter 'u' (either upper or lower case).

Hold up one card disc. As you do so, name the letter and encourage all the children to say it with you. Explain that you would like each child to show their letter to the rest of the group. Encourage all the children to say the letter (name or sound) as they see it. Read it with them and tell them that they must try not to smile as they do this, but that as soon as they see the letter 'u' they must give their biggest smile. Continue until all the children have shown their letters.

Support and extension
For younger children, just use the lower-case letters, and avoid any easily-confused letters, such as 'b' and 'd'. Give older children two letters each and invite them to show first one, then the other.

Home links
Provide parents and carers with a sheet of all the letters in the alphabet. Ask them to cut out the letters and display them around the house for their children to read. When they are using alphabetical indexes in address books or dictionaries, invite them to help their children to find and read the indexing letters.

Further ideas
■ Play the game again, but ask the children to each smile when they see the initial sound in their name.
■ Make letter people. Invite each child to paint one large letter on a sheet of A3 paper and to add features, arms, legs and hats.

Communication, language and literacy

In the beginning

Learning objective
To use language to re-create roles and experiences and encourage the use of expressions.

National Literacy Strategy
To be aware of story structures, especially consequences and the ways that stories are built up and concluded.

Group size
Four or more children.

What you need
Just the children.

What to do
Talk about the things that Clarine did on her first day at school, such as meeting the other children, playing games and painting. Explain that you would like the children individually to tell the rest of the group their memories of the first day that they met in the room. Continue by asking the children to try to remember if they were helped by anyone on that day. Perhaps someone showed them where the pencils were, or played a game with them?

Choose one of the children to narrate to the rest of the group what happened to them on that day. Encourage them to think of how they could begin their story and to try to sequence the events before deciding on a suitable ending. Invite the other children to take it in turns to tell their stories.

After all the children have told their stories, choose one of the events mentioned that involve helping someone. Invite the children to work in pairs or small groups (depending on the number of people in the event) to role-play the event that you chose. Encourage the children to think about what each of the people would feel. Once the children are happy with this, encourage them to sequence two or three events.

Support and extension
Encourage younger children to think of two things that they have done today and to sequence them in the right order. Invite older children to say more and to try to have a clear structure to their story.

Home links
Encourage parents and carers to help their children to retell popular stories, such as a picture book or a fairy story.

Further ideas
■ Stick a photograph of each of the children on to wooden spoons or clean, upturned empty yoghurt pots to make simple puppets. Encourage the children, in small groups, to retell the story of their first day in your setting using the puppets.
■ Make a group book based on the children's experiences, asking an adult to act as a scribe.

Communication, language and literacy

Learning objective
To use a pencil and hold it effectively to form recognizable letters, most of which are correctly formed.

National Literacy Strategy
To write letters using the correct sequence of movements.

Group size
Four to six children.

What you need
The photocopiable sheet on page 112; drawing and writing materials.

I like you

What to do
With the children, look at the pictures in the book and try to decide who each child is friends with. Ask the children to tell you if they have a best friend and, if so, what their name is and why they like them. They may suggest that their best friend always plays with them, tells them all their secrets or listens to them when they are upset.

Give each child a copy of the photocopiable sheet and some drawing and writing materials. Read through the words on the sheet together. Ask each child to write the name of their best friend and one reason why they like them on to the appropriate spaces on their sheet. Encourage them to carefully write the words, thinking about how to form each letter as they do so. Check their pencil grip as necessary. You may need to write the words out first so that the children can either write over them or use them for help with spelling.

Finally, invite each child to add illustrations of themselves and their friend below the text.

Support and extension
Invite younger children to just write the initial letters of the words. Encourage older children to think of the size of the letters and the length of the ascenders and descenders.

Home links
Give each child a copy of the A4 card with their name on (see 'Further ideas') and invite them to take it home so that they can trace over it with their parents or carers.

Further ideas
■ Write each child's name on to a sheet of A4 card. Mark the starting-point of each letter, and number in sequence each of the strokes needed to form the letter.
■ Put the children into pairs. Make sure that each child can correctly write one letter. Ask the children to take it in turns to watch each other write the letter that they know how to write and to check that they are using the correct sequence of movements.

Bigger feet, smaller hands

Learning objective
To use language such as 'bigger' or 'smaller' to compare quantities.

National Numeracy Strategy
To use language such as 'bigger' or 'smaller', 'longer' or 'shorter', to compare two quantities by making direct comparisons of lengths or masses.

Group size
Four to six children.

What you need
Paper; writing materials; two teddy bears of a similar size.

What to do
Look with the children at the pictures that show Clarine with her grandfather and talk about the difference in size between their hands, heads and bodies.

Show the children the teddy bears that you have selected. Invite them to say which bear they think is the biggest and which is the smallest. Put the two bears next to each other on top of a flat surface and help the children to compare the sizes and find out which bear really is the biggest and which is the smallest.

Divide the children into pairs. Invite them to compare some of their body parts, such as their arms, hands, legs and feet, to discover who has the biggest, or the smallest, of whatever they have chosen to measure. Encourage them to align the body parts and put the extremities together when comparing them.

Ask the children to record their results. Draw a straight line near the edge of a large piece of paper (alternatively, they could use the edge of the paper itself). Help them to draw around each body part that they compared by putting the part on the paper and making sure that an extremity of the body part touches the line (or edge). Write the owner's name by each body part. Encourage the children to share their findings with each other and to compare their results.

Support and extension
Ask younger children to just compare body parts and not to record the results. Invite older children to measure each of the body parts using non-standard measures, such as small plastic bricks, pencils or square wooden beads, to find out just how much larger or smaller the body parts are.

Home links
Ask parents and carers to encourage their children to compare sizes of objects at home, such as their newest clothes with some older clothes.

Further idea
■ **Make stretched handprints. Invite each child to paint one of their palms and to make a handprint on a large piece of paper. Then ask them to repeat the printing, sliding their hand along the paper to make as long a print as possible.**

Mathematical development

Learning objective
To use language such as 'more' or 'less' to compare two numbers.

National Numeracy Strategy
To use language such as 'more' or 'less', 'greater' or 'smaller', to compare two numbers and say which is more or less, and to say a number which lies between two given numbers.

Group size
Four children.

What you need
Two small plastic bowls; cherries (either real or pretend); paper; writing materials.

One for you

What to do
Show the pictures of Clarine sharing cherries with children in her class. Explain to the children in your group that you would like them to be just like Clarine and to share out some cherries.

Give the children the plastic bowls and the cherries. Invite one of them to divide the cherries between the two bowls, but not by counting them one by one. Help the children to decide whether the bowls look as if they have the same amounts of cherries in them or not. The children may suggest that one bowl has more, or one bowl has less. Next, take the cherries out of one bowl and count them. Write the quantity of cherries on a piece of paper. Do the same with the cherries in the other bowl. Encourage the children to say which of the numbers they think is bigger, and which is smaller. Invite them to suggest a number that is in between those numbers.

Combine all the cherries again and ask another child to try to share the cherries. Continue as before, counting the cherries, writing the numbers down and comparing them until all the children have tried sharing the cherries.

Support and extension
For younger children, initially use ten cherries, then gradually increase to 20 cherries. Invite older children to compare larger quantities of cherries.

Further idea
■ Give the children a set of traditional balance scales and some identical objects, such as empty cotton reels. Encourage the children to put equal quantities of the objects on each side of the scales to make them balance.

Home links
Invite parents and carers to play 'I'm thinking of a number' with their children. The adult thinks of a number, which the child has to guess. The adult must give clues by saying whether the child's guess was more or less than the number that they were thinking of.

Lots of friends

Learning objective
To say and use number names in order in familiar contexts.

National Numeracy Strategy
To recite the number names in order, continuing the count forwards or backwards from a given number.

Group size
Four or more children.

What you need
The photocopiable sheet on page 108.

What to do
Explain to the children that you would like them to play a game with their friends, just as Clarine plays a ball game with Lisa and her friends. Invite them to form a circle, holding hands and facing into the middle of the circle. Read aloud the words on the photocopiable sheet. Tell the children that you will read the words again, but that this time you would like them to join in as you say them. Then sing the tune to them.

Give each child a number from 1 to 10 and ask them to try to remember their number. Depending on the size of your group, some of the numbers may be given to more than one child.

Explain that when you call out a number you would like everyone with that number to step forwards into the circle. Call out two or three numbers between 1 and 10 and wait for the children with those numbers to move forwards. If the children forget their numbers, give them a piece of paper with their number written on.

Sing the song all the way through, with each child stepping forwards as

their number is sung. Try singing the song faster or more slowly, so that the children have to move accordingly. You could also try reversing the sequence of numbers, or counting from a different starting number.

Support and extension
Change the numbers in the song, using numbers to 5 for younger children. Practise counting forwards and backwards to 5 before using numbers to 10. Encourage older children to count forwards and backwards from a larger number, such as 20 or 30.

Home links
Encourage parents and carers to use numbers in sequence with their children by singing number songs or counting steps.

Further idea
■ **Make a collection of favourite counting songs, such as 'Five Currant Buns' (Traditional), and rewrite them so that the counting is opposite to what is expected, for example, beginning with one currant bun instead of five.**

Personal, social and emotional development

Learning objective
To consider the consequences of their words and actions for themselves and others.

Group size
Four or more children.

What you need
Flip chart or easel and paper; marker pen.

Be nice

What to do
After reading the book to the children, ask them if they can remember how Clarine tried to make friends. Write down their suggestions, such as offering the other children cherries, or taking a ball, on the flip chart or easel.

Read out the first item on the list of suggestions. Encourage the children to say whether they think that it was a nice way to try to make friends, or if it would not help Clarine to make friends. Write the children's decision next to the item on the flip chart. Consider the rest of the items on the list in the same way.

Invite the children to take it in turns to think of one nice action that they could do towards someone else, such as helping them to put their coat on, sharing a book or tidying up some toys with them. You may want to write the children's ideas down on the flip chart. Throughout, encourage the children to think about the feelings of other people.

Support and extension
Invite younger children to each think of just one nice thing that they could do for another person. If they find it difficult, ask them to think of something that they might like someone to do to them. Encourage older children to think of a wide range of suggestions, and to try not to repeat something that has already been said.

Home links
Invite parents and carers to help their children to draw a picture at home of something that they could do to help someone else. Ask the children to bring their pictures in to talk about them with the rest of the group.

Further ideas
■ Help the children to write their ideas down in a book.
■ Play 'Consequences'. Make a set of cards with either 'nice' or 'nasty' written on each of them. Sit the children in a circle, facing inwards. Give each child a card, alternating between 'nice' and 'nasty'. Invite them to tell a story and to think of a 'nice' or a 'nasty' action to continue the story, depending on what word is on their card. Use some of the children's helpful ideas to stimulate role-play.

Personal, social and emotional development

You and me

Learning objective
To take turns and be sensitive to the feelings of others.

Group size
Pairs of children.

What you need
The photocopiable sheet on page 113; thin card; dice; two different-coloured counters for each child.

What to do
Read the book and talk about Clarine's actions with the other children. Discuss which ones were friendly, such as sharing the cherries, and which were not, such as taking the ball. Invite the children to suggest other friendly and unfriendly actions.

Copy the photocopiable sheet on to thin card. Give a copy to each pair of children and a counter to each child. Ask them to choose a different star to put it on and invite the children to decide who will start first. The first player rolls the dice and moves their counter a number of spaces equal to the number on the dice. If the player lands on an empty space, the other child has their turn. If they land on a happy face, ask them to think of a way that they could be nice to someone. If they land on a sad face, invite them to suggest an unfriendly action, such as taking somebody's ball. When the player has finished talking, the next player can have their turn.

Encourage the children to use events from the story or their own experiences for ideas of friendly and unfriendly behaviour. Invite them to take it in turns to move around the grid until

they both land on the same space, or until they have played for a predetermined length of time.

Support and extension
Invite younger children to take turns and move around the grid without suggesting any actions. Encourage older children, whenever they land on a face, to try to suggest an appropriate action that has not already been mentioned in that game.

Home links
Encourage the children to play turn-taking games such as 'Snakes and ladders' and 'Noughts and crosses' at home. Invite parents and carers to ask them to take turns to carry out safe tasks at home, such as folding clothes (saying, for example, 'You fold this jumper and I'll fold the next') or setting the table ('You do the forks and I'll do the knives').

Further ideas
■ **Look at the poster showing members of the family and friends and invite the children to suggest possible reasons why each of the people in the pictures is smiling.**
■ **Make a collection of games that will encourage the children to take turns, such as 'Dominoes' or 'Lotto'.**
■ **Compile a songbook of turn-taking songs and rhymes such as 'Five Currant Buns' (Traditional).**

Knowledge and understanding of the world

I remember when

Learning objective
To find out about past and present events in their own lives and in those of their families and other people they know.

Group size
Four or more children.

What you need
Just the children.

What to do
Look at each of the characters in the book in turn (Clarine's Mum, Dad and Grandpa), and talk about how all those people tried to help Clarine by telling her about their own experiences (sharing fruit, playing ball and smiling).

Explain to the children that you would like each of them to think of something that one person in their family has done to help them. Before you start the activity, tell them that you would like the other children to ask relevant questions to the child who is speaking, to find out more about how they were helped and by whom.

Either begin the activity yourself or choose one of the children to start. Encourage the children who are listening to find out as much as possible from the speaker by asking questions such as, 'Where did they help you?', 'What did the helper look like?' or even 'Was their help useful?'. Continue until each child has had an opportunity to tell the other children about one way in which someone in their family has helped them.

Support and extension
Encourage younger children to concentrate on just telling their stories, rather than asking lots of questions. Invite older children to give longer accounts and to try to give more information about the event, such as how old they were when it happened, how long ago it took place, or why they needed help.

Home links
Invite parents and carers to find photographs of some family members who have helped them and to talk with their children about how they were helped by them.

Further ideas
■ Invite helpers around your setting to talk to the children about how they have been helped in the past by various family members.
■ Fold a sheet of A3 paper in half and then in half again. On the front cover, write 'My family helps me'. Open up the book and write 'Who?' at the top of the first page, 'Where?' at the top of the next page, and 'What?' on the back cover. Give a book to each child and help them to write down how they have been helped by answering each of the questions.

Knowledge and understanding of the world

Make it round

Learning objective
To select the tools and techniques they need to shape, assemble and join materials they are using.

Group size
Four to six children.

What you need
Three or four small balls made from a variety of materials; pieces of fabric, paper, card and clay; clay tools; scissors; glue; glue spreaders; sticky tape; paints; felt-tipped pens.

Further ideas
■ **Challenge each child to make a cubic box with the correct number of sides and corners using a material of their choice.**
■ **Put a head on each of the children's balls and a weight inside it to make a figure that will not fall over when pushed gently.**

What to do
Talk about how Clarine uses a ball to try to make friends towards the end of the story – she catches another child's ball and throws it through a hoop. Explain to the children that you would like each of them to make a ball that they could give to a friend. Invite each child to talk about who they would like to make their ball for. Ask them to tell you what they think they could use to make it, for example, clay, paper, card or fabric.

Help each child to select the materials that they need to make their ball, then to get the appropriate tools to shape it. These will vary depending on the materials that the children have collected.

Encourage each child to think carefully about the shape of the ball as they make it. If necessary, invite them to look closely at the balls that you have collected. The children may also need to think about joining the materials, especially if they are using clay as they will need to make their balls in two halves.

Once the balls are finished, and dry if applicable, invite the children to decorate them.

Support and extension
Give younger children a limited choice of materials and tools with which to make their balls. Invite older children to select all their resources and materials, and to discuss whether the materials that they chose were suitable for the task.

Home links
Ask parents and carers to invite their children to help them to use sticky tape, paper glue and paper clips.

Catch hoopla

Learning objective
To handle balls with increasing control.

Group size
Groups of three children.

What you need
A large hoop for each group; a soft ball for each group.

What to do
Explain to the children that you would like them to play a game where they will take it in turns to throw a ball through a hoop. Divide the children up into groups of three. Ask each group to stand in a line, with the children at the ends facing the child in the middle, and with a space of at least one metre in between.

Give each middle child a hoop and ask them to hold it at the side of their body at waist height with both hands. Invite the other two children in each group to take it in turns to throw the ball to each other through the hoop. After they have thrown the ball to each other once, ask one of them to swap places with the child in the middle so that they can try to throw the ball through the hoop. Continue until each child has tried holding the hoop and throwing the ball through the hoop a few times.

Support and extension
Invite younger children to work in pairs, one child holding the hoop while the other throws the ball, and then to swap roles. Encourage older children to try using a smaller hoop, or have a relay: line up two or three children with hoops and some children in between without hoops, and challenge them to pass the ball from one end of the line to the other, throwing it through the hoops as quickly as possible.

Home links
Invite parents and carers to make skittles for their children, using old, clean plastic bottles and a ball of screwed-up paper wound around with sticky tape.

Further idea
■ **Roll the balls through the hoops instead of throwing them. Ask one child to hold a hoop with its rim on the floor for another child to roll the ball through. (Make small cardboard ramps to fit over the rim to make sure that the ball rolls smoothly.)**

You're my friend

Learning objective
To move with confidence, imagination and in safety.

Group size
Four or more children.

What you need
Large, empty floor space; several coloured bands for each child.

What to do
Look at the pictures in the book showing Clarine and a ball. Talk together about what Clarine does with the ball and how she tries to use it to make friends. Explain to the children that you would like them to play a game together where they all have to make friends with one another.

Encourage the children to spread out in the large, empty space. Choose one child (the leader) to start the game and give them all the coloured bands. Ask them to wear one of the coloured bands. Explain that when you give a signal you would like all the children to move around the space. Next, the leader should try to tap someone on the shoulder, and the child who was tapped must stand still. The leader must give that child a band to wear and some bands to carry. Then the child who has been given a band and the leader must hug each other and both

say to each other 'Friend!'. While the rest of the group continues to move around the space, the child who has been given a band tries to tap another child on the shoulders, gives them a band to wear and some bands to carry, calls them 'Friend!', and so on until everyone in the room is wearing a band.

Support and extension
Shorten the game for younger children by choosing three or four children to wear the coloured bands from the start. Extend the game for older children by having 'safe places': mark a few squares on the floor where the children can have immunity from being tapped for up to a count of ten; at the end of the count, they must leave the safe place.

Home links
Encourage parents and carers to challenge their children to find things around the home, such as three blue objects, and to touch them all as quickly as possible.

Further idea
■ Play the game telling the children how fast you would like them to walk, or asking them to move only in a certain direction, such as sideways or backwards.

Creative development

Friendly dance

Learning objective
To use their imagination in music and dance.

Group size
Four or more children.

What you need
Large, empty floor space; the photocopiable sheet on page 109.

What to do
As you look at each picture in the book, ask the children to say if they think that the characters in it are friends or not. Can they tell you why they think that they are friends? For example, they could suggest that they are holding hands or playing games together. Then invite the children to talk about the friendly behaviour that they adopt towards their own friends, such as hugging them or smiling at them.

Read through the words of the song on the photocopiable sheet. Read the words again and invite the children to join in with you. Sing the words with the music two or three times and encourage the children to sing too.

Call out each action in turn from the song and ask them to suggest an appropriate movement for it. For example, for 'Come and play', they could beckon to each other, and for 'Dance with me' they could hold hands with their arms crossed and dance around in a circle.

Encourage the children to find a partner and to stand together in the large, empty space. Explain that you will call out one part from the song and that you would like them, in their pairs, to make the agreed movement for each action. Repeat two or three times.

Once the children are comfortable with the actions and movements in the song, slowly sing the song together, with the partners doing each action at the appropriate part of the song. Encourage the children to think about how they use the various parts of their bodies and their facial expressions.

Support and extension
Invite younger children to start with trying the movements just for the first three actions in the song. Give older children the opportunity to think of their own actions to accompany the song.

Further idea
■ **Add pieces of small equipment, such as scarves or balls, to the dance.**

Home links
Ask parents and carers to play a variety of styles of music at home and to encourage their children to listen to it and make up their own dances.

People pictures

Learning objective
To use their imagination in art and design.

Group size
Four to six children.

What you need
Rolls of pale, coloured thin paper; drawing and painting materials; offcuts of cloth and paper; large wooden blocks; thick pencils; scissors.

What to do
Read the book and talk about which children are Clarine's friends. Then ask the children to tell you who their friends are. Unroll one of the large rolls of paper. Weight the end of the paper down with the wooden blocks to prevent the paper from rolling back. Ask one of the children to lie on their back on the paper and demonstrate how to carefully draw around them with a thick pencil. Once the child stands up, there will be a life-size outline of a child on the paper.

Ask the children to find a friend and pair up. Give each pair two large pieces of paper and a thick pencil. Invite the children to take it in turns to draw around each other on to the paper. They could lie in poses, pretending to be helping someone, for example, a firefighter putting out a fire with a hose, or a vet holding a dog. When all the children have been drawn around, help them to cut out their friends' shapes.

Encourage each child to think about how they would like to paint their picture of the friend that they drew around. Ideas of how they could finish their picture might include painting the clothes that their friend is wearing, or showing the friend in the clothes that a person who helps us might wear, such as a firefighter or police officer's uniform. The children could also use fabric and paper offcuts to add to their pictures.

Support and extension
Invite younger children to work in pairs to complete one picture between them. Let older children work more independently, mixing their own paints and fetching their own resources.

Home links
Encourage parents and carers to let their children draw and paint at home to make pictures for greetings cards or signs for doors.

Further idea
■ **Invite the children to make body-part compilation pictures by drawing around the head, torso and limbs of different children on one large piece of paper to make a full-sized 'portrait'.**

Role-play

In the classroom

Learning objective
To have a developing awareness of their own needs, views and feelings and be sensitive to the needs, views and feelings of others.

Group size
Four to six children.

What you need
Two small tables or two large cardboard boxes; four small chairs; area for the teacher with a chair; collection of picture and information books; four small coat hooks and four coats or jackets; exercise books; card for making labels; set of name cards for all the children in the group.

What to do
Make a 'classroom' in the role-play area, using the tables (or boxes) and chairs. Put the hooks on the wall and hang the coats on them. Leave exercise books and pencils on the tables, and the name cards of the children that you would like to use the role-play area.

Read the book and explain that the role-play area is now a 'classroom', just like the one in the book. Invite one of the children to be a teacher and the rest of the children to be the pupils.

Encourage the children to think of the types of jobs that the teacher does, such as welcoming new children, helping pupils with their work or reading stories.

Next, invite the children to think about the types of things that they would do if they were in school, such as writing in books, listening to stories and playing together. You may need to remind them that there should be only one teacher (unless they have a helper).

Invite some of the children to pretend to be new to the group. Encourage the 'teacher' to introduce the new children to the rest of the group, and invite the children to try to make friends with one another and to think about the needs of both the 'old' and the 'new' children.

Support and extension
Invite younger children to introduce just one 'new' child. Encourage older children to try to use the questions and language of teachers and pupils.

Further ideas
■ Invite the children to paint pictures to hang on the walls of the 'classroom'.
■ Ask the 'teacher' to make sure that each 'new' child has somewhere to hang their coat, some books to write in and a card with their name on it.
■ Use the picture of the teacher on the poster that depicts people who help us in the community as a stimulus, and invite the children to take it in turns to lead a 'show and tell' session. Encourage the 'teacher' to ask the children questions about their chosen object or story.

Home links
Ask parents and carers to talk with their children about their memories of starting a new school.

Chapter 2

🚸 Freddie Visits the Doctor

This story of Freddie and his teddy bear visiting the doctor can be used to encourage children to talk about their own experiences of going to the doctor's. It can also prompt them to talk about people who help them to stay healthy, such as family members and doctors. The simple sequence of events from leaving home to coming back with some medicine can also be explored.

🚸 Using the book

The re-sequencing of events in the book, as told by Freddie's teddy bear, begins the Communication, language and literacy activities. The children can pretend to be doctors and write a prescription for a sick bear, and make up rhymes about someone who is ill and then gets better.

The theme of sick bears is continued in the Mathematical development section. To keep their bears warm, the children are invited to decorate cardboard hats and scarves with coloured stripes to make patterns. They are encouraged to use different-sized spoons to measure out quantities of water, which can then be compared. They are also invited to read numbers and make sure that 'unwell' bears receive their medicines.

The Personal, social and emotional activities invite the children to put on some outdoor clothes in readiness for going on a car journey to the doctor's, and to describe a time when they have visited a doctor.

In the Knowledge and understanding of the world activities, the children are invited to make small teddy-bear-sized benches for a waiting-room, using materials that they choose themselves. They also find out what a stethoscope is for and how to use it.

In Physical development, the children talk about things that they can do to stay healthy and play a 'Lotto'-style game. They are also invited to 'rescue' teddy bears and 'take them to the doctor's', moving around a large, open space, to discuss how this makes them feel.

In Creative development, paper plates are used to make faces that look ill, and some wrinkled noses are guaranteed as the children are invited to smell some strong-smelling substances.

In the role-play activity, the children have the opportunity to be patients and receptionist in a surgery's waiting-room.

Communication, language and literacy

Bear is ill

Learning objective
To retell a narrative in the correct sequence, drawing on language patterns of stories.

National Literacy Strategy
To notice the difference between spoken and written forms through retelling known stories; to compare 'told' versions with what the book 'says'.

Group size
Four to six children.

What you need
The photocopiable sheet on page 114; tape recorder with speakers and a microphone; blank tape; scissors; flip chart or easel and paper; Blu-Tack.

What to do
In preparation for the activity, record on to a blank tape yourself reading aloud the photocopiable sheet. Then copy the sheet and cut out each sentence.

Encourage the children to talk about the events in the book and the order in which they happened. Tell them that you would like them to listen to a story on the tape recorder that describes what the bear in the book might have remembered about the trip to the doctor's. Play the tape that you have made all the way through, then invite the children to comment on it. Was the story on the tape like the one in the book? Did it make sense?

Play the tape again, pausing after the first event. Find the matching sentence from the cut-up photocopiable sheet and use Blu-Tack to stick it on to the flip chart. Ask the children if this really was the first thing that happened in the book. Play the next event on the tape, find the appropriate sentence and put it underneath the first sentence on the flip chart. Repeat for each event on the tape.

When all the sentences are on the flip chart, help the children as a group to order the events into the sequence that they appeared in the book.

Support and extension
For younger children, compare the sentences on the sheet with the pictures and words in the book. Ask older children to listen to the story two or three times and to decide verbally on a sequence of events. Then display the sentences on the flip chart in the order that they have chosen.

Home links
Encourage parents and carers to discuss with their children the sequence of events in books that they have read together.

Further idea
■ Invite the children to retell the story pictorially as a comic strip.

Communication, language and literacy

Patient bears

Learning objective
To use their phonic knowledge to write simple regular words and make phonetically plausible attempts at more complex words.

National Literacy Strategy
To identify and write initial and dominant phonemes in spoken words.

Group size
Four to six children.

What you need
The photocopiable sheet on page 115; selection of drawing and writing materials; small circular, square and rectangular stickers.

What to do
Read the book and talk about how we visit the doctor when we are ill and how sometimes we need medicine to make us better. The doctor then writes a prescription listing the medicine that we need, which we take to the chemist who finds it for us.

Invite the children to pretend to be doctors. Give each child a copy of the photocopiable sheet. Explain that the bear on the sheet is the 'patient', who is ill. Help each child to think of a name for their bear and to write it in the appropriate space on the sheet.

Encourage each child to suggest why their bear might be ill. Ideas could include a tummy ache, sore head or itchy arm. Help the children to put coloured stickers (plasters and bandages) on to the parts of the bears that need to get better.

Ask each child to 'write' their diagnosis and the treatment needed underneath the bear at the bottom of the page using their own level of writing. Encourage them to say aloud each word, listening carefully for each of the initial and dominant sounds before writing them. Invite them to try to use their phonic knowledge to write words that they are unsure about.

Ask each child to finish their prescription by signing their name in the appropriate space on the sheet. They could either write their name normally or try an adult-style signature.

Support and extension
Invite younger children to label each sticker with the name of the body part that it is stuck on. Encourage older children to write in sentences or to have multiple ailments for their bears.

Home links
Encourage parents and carers to help their children to set up a hospital corner at home where their children can pretend to bandage their toys and try to make them better.

Further idea
■ Try the activity with a real teddy bear, using bandages rather than stickers.

Communication, language and literacy

How are you today?

Learning objective
To make up their own rhymes.

National Literacy Strategy
To recognize, explore and work with rhyming patterns.

Group size
Four to six children.

What you need
The photocopiable sheet on page 106.

What to do
Discuss how the doctor and chemist help to make Freddie better by listening to his chest and giving him some medicine. Tell the children that you are going to read some rhymes and that you would like them to listen carefully. Read the photocopiable sheet.

Ask the children to tell you what they thought of the poems. Did anyone notice that each of the poems starts with someone who is ill and finishes with that person getting better? Explain to the children that some of the words in the poems rhyme: although they have a different sound at the beginning, they end with the same sound. Give the children two or three examples of pairs of rhyming words from the poems on the photocopiable sheet. Tell them that you are going to read the poems again, and that you would like them to say if they hear any rhyming words.

Invite the children to verbally make up their own poems about being ill and getting better. They can be either about real illnesses, such as Freddie's sore throat, or something that the children have had, such as a cold or chicken pox. Alternatively, the poems may be based on imaginary people or nursery-rhyme characters with imaginary illnesses.

Encourage the children to try to use rhyming words in their poems. Give them the opportunity to use the rhyming words on the sheet if they want to. When they have finished, invite them to share their rhymes with the rest of the group.

Support and extension
Invite younger children to make up rhymes with repetitions, such as 'doctor, doctor'. Encourage older children to use more rhymes or rhyming patterns in their poems.

Home links
Give each child a copy of the photocopiable sheet to take home and share with their parents or carers.

Further ideas
■ **Read nonsense poems to the children and invite them to clap out each of the syllables in them.**
■ **Give the children the opportunity to record their poems on to an audio tape.**

Mathematical development

Wrap up warmly

Learning objective
To talk about, recognize and re-create simple patterns.

National Numeracy Strategy
To talk about, recognize and re-create simple repeating patterns.

Group size
Four to six children.

What you need
A4-sized card shapes of woolly bobble hats and scarves; strips of plain fabric or card (long enough to fit across the width of the card hat and scarf shapes) in red, yellow, blue and green; glue; glue spreaders; scissors; aprons; newspapers.

What to do
Show the children the pictures that reveal Freddie and his teddy bear wearing their hats and scarves. Talk with the children about the sequence of colours on each of the scarves and hats.

Explain to the children that you would like them to make hats and scarves for the bear in the story, and to decorate them with coloured stripes to make a pattern.

Ask each child to put on an apron and to choose either a card hat or a card scarf. Show them the fabric or card strips. Invite them to choose three colours and to put the strips underneath each other on their hat or scarf to make three stripes. Then ask them to use more strips in the same colours to make a repeating pattern. Encourage them to talk about the sequencing of the strips and to predict what they will need to continue the pattern.

When the children have finished their patterns, help them to glue the strips on to their card shapes. Some of the strips may be too long for the card outline, so the children will need to carefully trim the edges to make them fit on to their scarves or hats.

Support and extension
Invite younger children to begin by alternating two colours to make a repeating pattern. Encourage older children to use more than three colours for their scarves or hats.

Home links
Invite parents and carers to help their children to search for patterns around the home, such as on wall tiles or floor coverings.

Further ideas
■ Provide the children with a wide variety of gummed or felt shapes, sequins and other small, flat objects in different colours. Invite them to repeat the activity above using the various shapes and colours to make different patterns.
■ Give the children paper strips of two contrasting colours. Show them how to weave these over and under each other to make a check pattern.

Mathematical development

Time for your medicine

Learning objective
To use language such as 'greater' and 'smaller' to compare quantities.

National Numeracy Strategy
To use language such as 'more' or 'less', 'longer' or 'shorter', to compare two quantities by making direct comparisons of lengths or masses, and by filling and emptying containers.

Group size
Four to six children.

What you need
Two identical small, transparent plastic containers (clean babies' bottles are ideal); aprons; selection of different-sized spoons (two of each size); large jug of water with two or three drops of food colouring.

What to do
Read the book and explain that medicines such as Freddie's pink medicine have to be measured with a spoon. Remind the children that they should only take medicine when a doctor or their carer says that they can.

Help the children to put on their aprons. Encourage them to order the spoons that you have selected according to size, and explain that they are going to try to find out how much liquid each spoon can hold.

Invite one of the children to put five spoonfuls of coloured water from the jug into one of the containers. Ask another child to put five spoonfuls of coloured water, using a different-sized spoon, from the jug into the other container. Ask the children to put the containers next to each other and to say if they have more, less or the same amount of water inside them.

Challenge the children, two at a time, to try to put the same quantity of coloured water into each container, first by using the same-sized spoons, and then by using different-sized spoons, one size for each container. Encourage the children to compare and talk about the quantities of water in the containers regularly. Continue until all the children have tried the activity.

Support and extension
For younger children, provide just two sizes of spoons. Give older children two more containers and encourage them to pour water from one container into a new container, then to compare water levels in the old and new containers.

Further idea
■ Challenge the children to put as much water as they can during a count of 10 into each container, then compare the quantities of water in the containers.

Home links
Invite parents and carers to find three different-sized spoons at home and to help their children to compare the amount of water that each of them can hold.

Mathematical development

Matching numbers

Learning objective
To recognize numerals 1 to 9.

National Numeracy Strategy
To recognize numerals 1 to 9.

Group size
Up to nine children.

What you need
Nine teddy bears; nine paper bags; nine small boxes that will each fit into one of the paper bags; marker pen; 27 white sticky labels.

What to do
Read the book and tell the children that the chemist reads the prescription that the doctor gives us, then finds the medicine that we need. The medicine is usually in a paper bag with our name on it, so that the chemist knows who to give it to.

Next, tell the children that you would like them to pretend to be chemists and to give some 'medicine' to teddy bears. Show the children the bears. Invite each child to think of a different number from 1 to 9. Write each number on three separate sticky labels, then put one label on a box, another on a bag and the last one on to a bear's tummy, making sure that each box, bag and bear has a different number from 1 to 9.

Put the bears into numerical order. Ask one of the children to choose a bear and to read the number that is on its tummy. Encourage them to find the matching box and bag, then to put the box in the bag and to give it to their bear. Continue until each of the children has had a turn and all the bears have had their medicine. Now muddle the bears and repeat the activity.

Support and extension
For younger children, use numbers between 1 and 5, with five bears, five boxes and five bags. Use more bears for older children, initially adding '0' and '10' before using numbers to 20.

Home links
Ask parents and carers to challenge their children to find and read numbers around the house, on clocks, video recorders, microwave ovens and other electrical equipment.

Further ideas
■ Label nine large boxes with the numbers 1 to 9. Spread the bears, small boxes and bags from the activity above around a large, empty space. Challenge the children to put each of the numbered items into the appropriately-numbered large boxes as quickly as possible.
■ Write out 'prescriptions' for the children, listing quantities of objects with illustrations, such as '4 buttons'. Ask the children to find all the items on their prescriptions.

Personal, social and emotional development

Let's get ready!

Learning objective
To dress and undress independently.

Group size
Four children.

What you need
Large, empty floor space; four chairs; four coats; four scarves; four pairs of gloves.

What to do
In the middle of the large, empty floor space, arrange the chairs into a square, with two chairs in front and two behind to make a 'car'. Put a coat, scarf and pair of gloves on each chair.

Talk with the children about the clothes that Freddie and the bear are wearing. Explain that, on a signal, you would like the children to rush to the 'car' and put on the sets of clothes (coat, scarf and pair of gloves) that were left for them, one on each chair. Once they have done this, they should sit on the 'car seats'.

Give the signal and encourage the children to put on the clothes. As soon as they are sat down, invite them to pretend to fasten their seatbelts. Talk them through a brief car trip through a town to a doctor's, describing the things that they might see on the way.

Once the children 'arrive', ask them to get out of the car and to run once around the edge of the large, empty space before getting back into the car. Then narrate a 'journey home' to the children and ask them to get out of the car and take their outdoor clothes off once they have 'arrived'. For large groups, have more than one car, with appropriate sets of clothes and challenge the children to be the quickest to get dressed. Make sure that each car is taken on a journey.

Support and extension
For younger children, provide only coats and scarves. Ask older children to wear extra items of clothing, such as a jumper and shoes. However, because this may make the children hot, ask them to walk around the empty space instead of running.

Home links
Ask parents and carers to encourage their children to get dressed by themselves. Invite them to give their children old clothes, especially with zips and buttons, for 'dressing up' in.

Further idea
■ Encourage the children to try getting dressed with one hand behind their back!

Personal, social and emotional development

What's on the plate?

Learning objective
To respond to significant experiences, showing a range of feelings when appropriate.

Group size
Four or more children.

What you need
Paper plates; marker pen.

What to do
Ask the children to give you words for as many different feelings as possible, such as happiness, anger or sadness. Draw a face on to each paper plate, showing one of the emotions named.

Read the book and sit the children in a circle, all facing towards the centre. Ask them if they have ever been to visit a doctor at a surgery, clinic or hospital. Invite each child to think of something that happened to them at the doctor's and how it made them feel. For example, Freddie was happy that the doctor could help him to feel better. Explain that you would like each child, in turn, to tell the others about the experience that they thought of, but without saying how it made them feel.

Begin the activity yourself. Think of a trip to the doctor's and how you felt emotionally, such as being upset that you had to stay in bed and rest. Find the plate that matches the emotion that you felt and put it face down on the floor, without showing it to the children. Narrate your experience to the group, without telling the children the emotion that you felt. Then invite them to decide how you felt. When they have guessed the emotion, show them the face that you hid beforehand.

Encourage each of the children, in turn, to think of an experience, hide the corresponding plate and talk about their visit to the doctor's for the rest of the group to guess how the visit made them feel.

Support and extension
Ask younger children to each think of either an occasion when they felt happy at the doctor's surgery, or one that made them feel sad. Invite older children to show each emotion with their faces.

Home links
Ask parents and carers to tell their children about a time when they were very happy, and an occasion when they felt very sad.

Further idea
■ **Look with the children at the double-page spread showing the waiting-room and discuss how each of the people in the picture might be feeling.**

Knowledge and understanding of the world

Build a bench

Learning objective
To build and construct with a wide range of objects, selecting appropriate resources and adapting their work where necessary.

Group size
Four to six children.

What you need
Two small bears, dolls or action figures for each child; variety of materials to make benches, such as card, boxes and wooden and plastic bricks; materials that could be used to join the items together, such as glue, scissors, staplers and sticky tape; materials for decorating the benches, such as pens, paints, gummed shapes, glitter, and paper and material offcuts.

What to do
Look in the book at the picture showing all the people sat on the bench in the waiting-room. Explain to the children that you would like each of them to make a bench for a pretend waiting-room for two bears (or dolls or action figures) to sit on. Show the children the bears.

Ask each child what they would like to make their bench from, and invite them to collect and bring back whatever they think they might need. Remind them that they may need to join the parts of their bench together, or they may want to decorate it, so they may need extra resources to do those things.

Help each child to decide on a size for their bench and to make it. Throughout, encourage the children to talk about what they are doing, and to get any other materials that they need to complete their benches.

Once all the benches are finished, you may want to test them to check that each will seat the two bears. You could also invite the children to predict which bench they think will be the strongest.

Support and extension
For younger children, limit the amount of resources available and try to only offer ones that they will be able to use to build successful benches. Invite older children to each make a design of their bench first, listing all the different resources needed.

Home links
Take photographs of all the benches and let the children bring their benches home. Encourage them to talk to their parents or carers about how they made them and what they used to build them.

Further idea
■ **Invite the children to make other bear-sized pieces of furniture, such as a table, reception desk, toy-box or magazine holder.**

Knowledge and understanding of the world

I can hear that

Learning objective
To ask questions about why things happen and how things work.

Group size
Four to six children.

What you need
A length of transparent plastic tubing and two plastic funnels for each child (make sure that the narrow end of each funnel will fit inside the plastic tubing); poster depicting people who help us.

What to do
Look in the book at the picture of the doctor listening to Freddie's chest with the stethoscope. Next, show the children the picture of the nurse and the teddy on the poster. Ask the children if they know what a stethoscope is for, then explain that it is for listening to the heart and lungs. Tell the children that the heart pumps blood all around the body, and that we need lungs to help us get plenty of air (oxygen).

Invite the children to tell you where their hearts and lungs are. Show each child the position of their heart and help them to put a hand on it. Next, ask the children why we use a stethoscope to listen to our heart and lungs. Encourage them to answer you with questions.

Put the children into pairs and invite them to take it in turns to listen to each other's hearts beating by putting an ear on to the other child's chest. Ask them to tell you what they heard, then explain that the end of the stethoscope that the doctor puts by their ear helps to make the sound louder.

Give each child a funnel. Invite them to hold it, putting its wide end on their friend's chest, and its narrow end next to (but not in) their ear. Ask the children if the beating sounds louder.

Next, explain that the tubing helps to carry sounds to the earpiece in the stethoscope. Help each child to put a length of tubing on to the narrow end of their funnel and invite them to listen to their partner's heartbeat again.

Support and extension
Suggest possible questions to younger children. Encourage older children to try to create their own stethoscopes by using rolled-up paper and paper cones.

Home links
Invite the children to take their 'stethoscopes' home to listen to their parents' or carers' heartbeats.

Further idea
■ Encourage the children to use their 'stethoscopes' to find as many things as possible around the room that make a noise.

Physical development

Stay healthy!

Learning objective
To recognize the importance of keeping healthy and those things which contribute to this.

Group size
Four children.

What you need
The photocopiable sheet on page 116; dotted dice; scissors.

What to do
Make eight copies of the photocopiable sheet and cut out each of the pictures on four of them. Read the book and explain to the children that we go to the doctor's when we feel ill, but that there are things that we can do to stay healthy, such as eating fruit and vegetables, having a good night's sleep and moving our bodies.

Look with the children at the pictures from one of the cut-up photocopiable sheets. Talk about each picture and how it shows something to do to help us stay well and healthy. Give each child an uncut photocopiable sheet and check that they know what the pictures, numbers and 'dice' are on it. Spread out, face up, the individual pictures from the cut-up photocopiable sheets. Invite the children to take it in turns to roll the dice. The first child to roll a six starts the game.

Ask the first player to roll the dice, give the number of spots on it and find the matching dice on their sheet. Invite

them to find the corresponding individual picture from the cut-out pictures and to put it on top of the picture on their sheet. The next player has their turn. If a child rolls a number for a picture that they have already put on their sheet, the next child takes their turn. As the children play, encourage them to talk about the pictures that they find. Carry on until a child has covered all the pictures on their photocopiable sheet.

Support and extension
Provide lots of support to younger children when they are trying to find the matching dice and pictures. Encourage older children to play more independently.

Home links
Invite parents and carers to talk with their children about ways that they can stay healthy, such as washing their hands before eating, eating fruit and vegetables and brushing their teeth.

Further idea
■ **Enlarge the pictures and make them into a large dice. Roll the dice and invite the children to mime an appropriate action for whichever picture is showing on the dice.**

I'm hot

Learning objective
To recognize the changes that happen to their bodies when they are active.

Group size
Four or more children.

What you need
Large, empty floor space, or outdoor area; a teddy bear for each child.

What to do
Invite the children to say how they feel physically now. Ask them to sit on one side of the empty space, and put the bears on the opposite side. Explain that you are going to pretend that the teddy bears are ill and that you would like the children to move across the room in different ways to collect them and bring them back to where they were sitting, as if taking them to the doctor's.

Suggest that the teddy bears have sore throats. Encourage the children to walk across the room to pick up their bears and return to their space. Encourage them to say how they feel. Are they cold or warm?

Take the bears back across the room. Now suggest that they have fallen over and hurt their knees, and tell the children that you would like them to skip across the room to get their bears. After the children have skipped across the room and back again with the bears, ask them to describe how they feel now. Are any of them hot or slightly breathless?

Return the bears to the other side of the room. Tell the children that the bears have fallen over again, have each broken an arm and need to go to hospital. Invite the children to run to their bears, then back across the room. Ask how they feel now. Encourage them to compare how they feel now with how they felt before the game, and ask them to suggest why they feel hot (because they have been active).

Support and extension
Invite younger children to just compare sitting down with running across the room to take the bears to hospital. Show older children how to find their pulse and ask them to check it after each time that they have gone back and forth across the room.

Home links
Encourage parents and carers to help their children to think of all the different ways that they can be active, such as playing football or swimming.

Further idea
■ **Challenge the children to find out what activity makes them the hottest, such as running, climbing, hopping or crawling.**

Creative development

You look ill

Learning objective
To explore colour and texture in two or three dimensions.

Group size
Four to six children.

What you need
Paper plates; poster paints; paintbrushes; aprons; PVA glue; dried lentils or split peas; pieces of tissue paper; paper offcuts, wool and other materials that the children could stir into the paint or glue on to the plates.

Further ideas
■ **Give each child another plate, which can be stapled to the bottom of the first plate to make a body. Help them to glue or staple arms and legs made from strips of material or card to the sides and bottom of the body.**
■ **Make 'You look well' faces on paper plates.**

What to do
Look in the book at some of the pictures showing Freddie. Do the children think that Freddie looks ill? Invite them to suggest how you can see that someone is ill. Show them the picture of the waiting-room with all the patients sitting down and invite them to talk about which people look ill, and why.

Tell the children that you would like them to each make on a paper plate a face that looks ill. Give each child a paper plate and ask them to give you suggestions of how to make the face look ill. Spots might be an obvious option, or they could try making the face different colours – people are often told that they look green when they are ill.

Encourage the children to choose resources from the selection that you have prepared and to use their imagination to make their faces. Texture could be added to the plates by gluing on lentil 'spots', or wool for hair or a beard. Make faces more realistic and three-dimensional by screwing up paper for eyeballs or gluing a bottle top to the plate to make a nose. Encourage the children to make their faces as colourful as possible.

Support and extension
Invite younger children to just draw or paint their faces on to the plates. Encourage older children to find their own resources and to be more creative in the ways that they decorate their plates.

Home links
Ask parents and carers to give their children an old cardboard box and to help them to decorate it using paints, stickers or felt-tipped pens to make it an ill-looking face. Invite each child to bring their 'face' to the setting to show the other children.

All kinds of smells

Learning objective
To respond in a variety of ways to what they smell.

Group size
Four to six children.

What you need
Several small plastic tubs with lids; selection of strong-smelling substances, such as coffee, mustard, lemon juice, curry paste and so on (make sure that whatever you choose is non-toxic and safe for the children to handle).

What to do
Ask the children if they have ever been to a doctor's surgery, a hospital or a clinic. Talk to them about the distinctive smells that they can find in these places and explain that they smell like this because they are especially clean and hygienic.

Put one of the strong-smelling substances that you have selected into each tub. Make sure that the children do not see you while you do this. Put a lid on to each container.

Explain to the children that you are going to ask each of them, in turn, to shut their eyes and smell something. Ask one child to close their eyes. Take the lid off one tub and invite the child to smell its contents, their eyes remaining shut. Encourage them to say whether or not they like the smell and what product they think it comes from. Give the other children, one at a time, the opportunity to smell the tub too, with their eyes shut.

After all the children have smelled the tub's contents, show them what it was. Repeat for each of the smells.

Support and extension
For younger children, have fewer smells. For older children, include manufactured smells such as pot pourri or washing-up liquid.

Home links
Ask the children to find one thing at home that they like the smell of and to put a little bit of it in a plastic tub with an airtight lid. Invite the children to take it in turns to explain what their favourite smell is and why they like it.

Further idea
■ Dilute each of the substances, if applicable, with water. Dip small pieces of sponge into the substances with tongs. Make 'smelly pictures' by printing with the sponges (holding them in the tongs) on to cartridge paper. Colour the substances, if desired, by stirring a little powder paint into each tub.

Role-play

Waiting for the doctor

Learning objective
To use language to imagine and re-create roles and experiences.

Group size
Four to six children.

What you need
Four chairs or a bench; clock; potted plants; box of toys; small, low table; magazines; 'stay healthy' posters; desk and chair; telephone; diary; pens; a name card for each child; paper; A5 envelopes.

What to do
On one side of the role-play area, put the desk and chair for the receptionist. Leave the telephone, diary, pens, paper, name cards and envelopes on the desk. Next to one wall, put the bench or four chairs. Put the low table in a corner of the role-play area and put the magazines and potted plants on it. Display the posters and clock on the walls. Leave the box of toys on the floor.

Read the book and explain to the children that you would like them to take it in turns to be patients waiting to see a doctor. Talk with them about how the receptionist helps us by answering the telephone, making appointments, finding the patients' notes and telling the doctor who is to see him or her next.

Choose one of the children to be the receptionist. Invite the other children to be the patients and ask them why they want to see a doctor. Perhaps they have a cold, or a grazed knee or a bad cough.

Encourage each 'patient', in turn, to ring the receptionist and ask for an appointment. Help the receptionist to find the correct name card, then to arrange all the name cards into the order that the children are to see the doctor.

Ask the patients to sit in the waiting-room. Explain that people in waiting-rooms often read, play with toys or just talk to the other people waiting. Ask the receptionist to call out the name of a patient every few minutes and to tell them that the doctor is ready to see them.

Support and extension
Encourage younger children to draw on their own experiences of being in a waiting-room to help with their role-play. Show older children how to use bandages safely and encourage them to use these in their role-play.

Home links
Invite parents and carers to role-play visiting a doctor with their children.

Further idea
■ **Provide a small sand-timer and encourage the receptionist to time each appointment.**

Chapter 3

What Would We Do Without Missus Mac?

This book tells the story of the indispensable Missus Mac, a helper in a school, always there to help anyone. It is full of little incidents that children will easily relate to, such as grazing a knee, and it can be used for children to think about just how much people around them help them and of ways that they can help others. It also encourages them to think about their feelings for those people.

Using the book

The Communication, language and literacy activities begin with an opportunity for the children to ask politely for help from 'Missus Mac', using events in the book as a starting-point. Children can also write a letter to ask Missus Mac to stay on, or read simple sentences about their friends helping each other.

In Mathematical development, the children count passengers on to a bus in a simple game. They also make small fold-out books depicting various objects and people that they can see around them in the setting. Another number game, which encourages the children to add and subtract, invites them to give bags to Missus Mac.

In Personal, social and emotional development, the children put 'thank you' stars on to pictures of the people who have helped them, and they talk about how they can help others.

In Knowledge and understanding of the world, the children join together the pieces of a waistcoat and draw pictures of people, trees and animals looking older than at the beginning of their lives.

The Physical development activities invite the children to focus on how they interact with others, encouraging teamwork in a 'joined together' activity and pretending to be a crossing patrol attendant to help others to cross a pretend road safely.

In the Creative development activities, the children sing for their parents, carers and helpers in a special concert, and make a table tidy using cardboard boxes.

The role-play area is turned into a pretend swimming-pool by placing a 'pool', reception desk and changing area with towels, swimming costumes and armbands.

Communication, language and literacy

Could you help, please?

Learning objective
To speak clearly and audibly with confidence and control and show awareness of the listener by their use of conventions such as 'please' and 'thank you'.

National Literacy Strategy
To use knowledge of familiar texts to re-enact or retell to others, recounting the main points in correct sequence.

Group size
Four or more children.

What you need
Large, empty floor space; flip chart or easel and paper; marker pen.

Further ideas
■ Invite 'Missus Mac' to ask if anyone needs help, and the children to take turns to answer her.
■ Repeat the activity using favourite story characters.
■ Look with the children at the pictures on the poster showing friends and members of the family. Encourage each child to choose one of the people and to suggest something that that person could help them with.

What to do
Read the book to the children. On the flip chart, make a list, in sequence, of all the people that Missus Mac helped and how she helped them.

Invite the children to stand in a circle in the middle of the large, empty floor space. Choose a child to be Missus Mac and ask them to stand in the centre of the circle. Tell the children that you would like them, one at a time, to ask Missus Mac to help them. Then explain that you would like everyone to ask for help with something from the list on the flip chart.

Invite a child to begin the activity. Help them to read the first item on the list, then encourage them to ask Missus Mac to help them, for example, saying, 'Please, Missus Mac, can you help me to put the ribbon back in my hair?'. Ask 'Missus Mac' to mime the activity. Remind the child who asks to thank Missus Mac for her help.

Invite the child who wanted help to swap places with Missus Mac. The first Missus Mac returns to the circle. Continue with the next child asking Missus Mac to help them with the next activity on the list on the flip chart, and so on until everyone has had the opportunity to ask for help and to be Missus Mac.

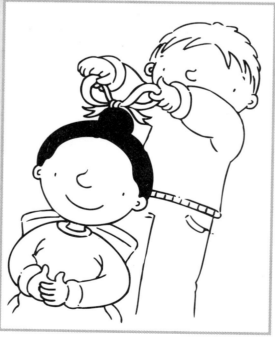

Support and extension
Invite younger children to ask Missus Mac for any help, not necessarily linked to an event in the book. Encourage them to speak as clearly and audibly as possible. Ask older children to give more information about how they want to be helped.

Home links
Encourage the children to retell the story in the book to their parents or parents, speaking clearly.

Communication, language and literacy

Learning objective
To attempt writing for different purposes, using features of different forms.

National Literacy Strategy
To use writing to communicate in a variety of ways, such as writing a letter.

Group size
Four to six children.

What you need
Drawing and writing materials; two discs in flesh-tone colours, each the diameter of a sheet of A4 card, for every child; stapler.

What to do
Read aloud up to the page where the children in the book shout, 'Missus Mac, please don't go!'. As you do so, draw the children's attention to the pictures that show Missus Mac helping others in a variety of ways. Ask them to tell you why they think that the children in the story want Missus Mac to stay. Encourage them to try to remember how Missus Mac helped the children in the story.

Give each child some drawing and writing materials and two card discs of the same colour. Using the pictures in the story of the unhappy faces or the children crying as a stimulus, invite the children to each draw a sad face on one of their discs. Explain that you would like each child to write a letter to Missus Mac asking her to stay. Talk with the children about the conventions that we normally use in a letter, such as 'Dear...', an ending and the name of the letter writer. Encourage each child to tell you one reason why they think Missus Mac should stay.

Next, ask the children to each write a letter to Missus Mac on their second card disc. Where possible, encourage them to write it in their own words. It could be as short as 'Missus Mac, please stay, Nisha'. Once the children have finished their letters, staple each set of discs at the top edge to make a card. Invite the children to share their cards with one another, then read them the remainder of the story.

Support and extension
Scribe letters for younger children, but encourage them to try to structure the letter according to letter conventions. Invite older children to write more words or sentences.

Home links
Invite parents and carers to help their children to 'write' letters at home for relatives and friends.

Further idea
■ **Ask the children to talk about one person that they would hate to be without. Encourage them to describe why they feel like this.**

Communication, language and literacy

Sunita helps Adam

Learning objective
To read a range of familiar and common words and simple sentences independently.

National Literacy Strategy
To read on sight a range of familiar words, including children's names and captions.

Group size
Four to six children.

What you need
60 blank playing cards; marker pen.

What to do
Write one word on each blank playing card: make a name card for every child, and on each of the remaining cards, write a selection of familiar and common words that the children can read. Try to include a mixture of nouns, verbs, adjectives and prepositions (naming, doing, describing and positional words) as well as 'a', 'the', 'helps' and 'helped'. Alternatively, use flashcards.

Read the book and talk about how Missus Mac helps the children in the story to read. Explain to the children that you would like them to make up and read some simple sentences about their friends. Begin by choosing two of the children in the group and encourage them to find the cards that have their names on. Put the two cards on a flat surface, leaving a space in between them.

Help the children to find a suitable verb (a 'doing' word) that could be put in the middle of the two names to make a simple sentence, such as 'helps'. Encourage the children to 'read' the sentence that they have made, for example, 'Sunita helps Adam'.

Invite the children to work in pairs to make sentences about each other using the cards, then to read them aloud. Encourage the children to help each other to read the words.

Support and extension
For younger children, replace the name cards with small photographs of each of them. To help them with the meaning of each word, draw a picture by each word (where possible). Alternatively, replace the nouns with real objects. Encourage older children to make longer sentences.

Home links
Give the children enough words to make two different sentences and let them take the words home with them. Encourage parents and carers to help their children to make sentences using the words.

Further ideas
■ Invite the children to draw pictures to illustrate each sentence that they make.
■ Provide blank playing cards and felt-tipped pens. Encourage the children, whenever they learn a new word, to write it on a card, then include it in a sentence.

Mathematical development

All aboard!

Learning objective
To count reliably up to 6.

National Numeracy Strategy
To count reliably up to ten everyday objects, giving just one number name to each object.

Group size
Four to six children.

What you need
Dice; the photocopiable sheet on page 117; pencils.

What to do
Show the children the illustrations of children crossing the road and sitting on the bus with Missus Mac. Read the text and talk about how she is helping by making sure that everyone crosses the road safely and gets on the bus.

Explain to the children that they are going to play a game where they must put some people (passengers) on to a bus. Give each child a copy of the photocopiable sheet and a pencil. Invite the children to take it in turns to roll the dice. The child who rolls the highest number plays first. They must roll the dice and call out the number on it. They then draw that number of passengers on to their bus – one person in each window. (To make the game faster, ask the children to just draw a smile and two eyes.) The next player then has their turn, rolls the dice and draws the correct number of people on their bus.

The winner of the game is the player who has drawn a face in every window on their bus. However, they must roll the exact number on the dice to fill up their bus with the right number of passengers for each of the spaces left.

Support and extension
For younger children, put stickers over the numbers on each face of the dice and label them '1', '2' and '3' twice, and ignore the rule that the children need to roll the exact number on the dice to finish the game. Simply end the game when a child has filled all the windows on their bus. Encourage older children to count more independently.

Home links
Ask parents and carers to encourage their children to count at home, such as how many trees there are in the garden, or oranges in a bowl.

Further idea
■ Put 11 chairs in a row, as if on a bus. Invite one child to be the driver and call out how many people can sit on the bus. Encourage the 'passengers' to count themselves.

Mathematical development

Look around you

Learning objective
To use everyday words to describe position.

National Numeracy Strategy
To use everyday words to describe position.

Group size
Four to six children.

What you need
Drawing and writing materials; flip chart or easel and paper; sticky tape; five squares of card for each child.

	Picture of something above the child	
Picture of something or someone to the left of the child	Picture of the child	Picture of something or someone to the right of the child
	Picture of something under the child	

What to do
Tape the squares together to make a cross shape (one square in the centre, and one square on each side of the central square). Fold them together to make a book.

Ask the children to think of as many words as possible that express where something is (positional words), such as 'up' and 'down'. Write the suggestions on the flip chart. Show the children one of the pages from the story, such as Missus Mac at the race. Invite one of them to point to Missus Mac. Choose one of the positional words from the list on the flip chart, such as 'down', and encourage the children to look for something in the picture that is 'down' compared to Missus Mac – for example, grass is 'down' from Missus Mac. Do this for each word on the flip chart.

Give each child a fold-out book and some drawing and writing materials. Demonstrate how the flaps can be unfolded and ask each child to draw a picture of themselves on the centre square.

Invite each child to look upwards and to tell you what they can see. Encourage them to draw this on the square above the picture of themselves. Next, ask them to look underneath them and to draw what they can see on the bottom square of their book. Then tell them that you would like them to look to their left and right and to draw one thing in each of those positions on each of the appropriate flaps (see diagram, left). Encourage them to talk about what they are drawing and the position of each item.

Support and extension
Encourage younger children to initially only use 'up', 'down' and 'by'. Invite older children to work more independently.

Home links
Send home a copy of the words that you wrote on the flip chart. Invite parents and carers to help their children try to find something in each of those positions.

Further idea
■ Cut out a variety of pictures from catalogues, such as linked to transport, and encourage the children to sort them into groups according to where they can be found.

Hold my bag

Learning objective
To begin to use the vocabulary involved in adding and subtracting.

National Numeracy Strategy
To begin to use the vocabulary involved in adding and subtracting.

Group size
Four to six children.

What you need
The photocopiable sheet on page 118; scissors; old mail-order clothing catalogues; thin card; thick card; glue; Blu-Tack.

What to do
Cut out pictures of bags from mail-order catalogues. Mount them on to thin card and cut each of them out. Put a small piece of Blu-Tack on the back of each bag. Glue the photocopiable sheet on to thick card and cut the 'helper' out. Glue an L-shaped piece of thick card to the back of the helper at the bottom to help it to stand up.

Look with the children at the picture of Missus Mac holding two school-bags. Show the children the picture of the helper that you have cut out and explain that you want them to give her some bags to hold. Begin by choosing one or two bags. Use Blu-Tack to stick them on to the helper, explaining how many bags you have given her and how many she is holding altogether. Invite the children to take it in turns to put one or two bags on to the helper, talking about how many they are adding and the total of bags that she has.

Once all the children have added their bags, take away one or two of the bags, telling the children how many you are taking away and how many are left. Invite them to take turns to do the same until there are no more bags on the picture of the helper.

Support and extension
Give younger children only ten bags between them to put on to the helper. Encourage older children to role-play why they are giving the bags to her, or taking them back.

Home links
Ask parents and carers to add and subtract at home with their children. For example, they could count groceries when they are putting their shopping away and say, 'There is one tin of beans in the cupboard; we have bought four more, so now we have five in total'.

Further idea
■ Give each child a number. Invite them to either add or take away bags so that the helper has the same number of bags as the number that they were given.

Personal, social and emotional development

You're a star!

Learning objective
To be sensitive to the needs, views and feelings of others.

Group size
Four to six children.

What you need
Photographs of each of the children, laminated or covered with sticky-backed plastic; Blu-Tack; drawing and writing materials; brightly-coloured stars cut from thin card with 'thank you' written on them; large display board at the children's height.

What to do
Look together in the book at the picture of Missus Mac giving some of the children gold stars in the playing field, and talk about why she is doing this. Ask the children to help you to use Blu-Tack to stick their photographs, leaving a space all the way around the edge of each photo, to the large display board.

Encourage each child to name somebody who has helped them. Use the illustrations in the book as a stimulus for ways that the children could have been helped. Has anyone helped them to fasten their shoes today?

Help the children to put some Blu-Tack on the back of each star and to stick them on to the photographs of the people who have helped them. Explain that you would like them to put a 'thank you' star on to the helper's photo each time that they are helped. You may want to ask the children to do this only once each day, such as at the end of the session. Encourage the children during the day to try to think of ways to help one another. Remind them that if they do not get a star on one day, they can try again on the next day. Monitor the activity to ensure that all the children get a star each.

Support and extension
Encourage younger children to draw a picture of someone, possibly a family member, who has helped them. Ask older children to write on their stars a few words on how they were helped.

Home links
Give each child a chart that has the days of the week on and a space underneath each day. Invite parents and carers to draw a happy face on the chart every day that their children help them.

Further idea
■ **Replace the stars with smiling faces. Encourage the children to talk about which people made them feel happy today.**

Personal, social and emotional development

Put it back

Learning objective
To understand that there needs to be agreed values and codes of behaviour for groups of people, including adults and children, to work together harmoniously.

Group size
Four or more children.

What you need
Flip chart or easel and paper; marker pen; drawing and writing materials; white A5 paper.

What to do
Show the children the picture in the book of the girl with glue stuck to the bottom of her shoe. Ask them to suggest ways in which that could have been prevented. Some may say that the lid of the tube of glue should have been put back on when it was not used any more, or that the glue should have been left in the middle of the table.

Choose an area in the room, such as the role-play area or the creative area. Ask the children to tell you if they have ever had any accidents there (or could think of some that might happen), such as falling on some clothes that were not hung up, or spilling water over a painting. Write the children's suggestions on the flip chart. You may want to draw a simple picture to illustrate each suggestion too. Choose one of the ideas on the flip chart and encourage the children to think of ways in which the accident could be prevented, such as leaving water pots in the middle of the table or putting lids on them.

Give each child a piece of A5 paper and some drawing and writing materials. Tell the children that you

would like them to draw on their paper themselves helping another person in one way, such as tying up their laces. Once the children have finished, invite them to share their pictures with the rest of the group and talk about what they have drawn. Encourage them to explain how the action that they have drawn is helpful.

Support and extension
Invite younger children to just draw a picture of themselves helping someone. Ask older children to each add an appropriate caption to their picture.

Home links
Encourage parents and carers to help their children to make a verbal list of the things that they have to do around the home, such as tidy up their toys before bedtime.

Further idea
■ **Help the children to make a list of all the group's 'rules'.**

Knowledge and understanding of the world

Learning objective
To select the tools and techniques they need to shape, assemble and join materials they are using.

Group size
Four children.

What you need
The photocopiable sheet on page 119; thin card; variety of resources for joining two things together, such as glue, sticky tape, staplers, split-pin fasteners, glue and paper clips; scissors; materials for decorating, such as stickers and felt-tipped pens.

Fasten it up!

What to do
Show the picture of Missus Mac helping a child with a stuck zip and talk with the children about when they have needed help to get dressed, such as when tying their laces or fastening buttons. Discuss why we have fasteners such as zips and laces.

Explain to the children that you would like them to make waistcoats (sleeveless jackets). Give each child a photocopiable sheet photocopied on to thin card and a pair of scissors. Help them to cut out each shape and to cut along the centre line of the front piece. Show them how they can put the two pieces for the front on top of the back piece. Talk with them about how they could join the pieces together at the sides to keep all the parts of the waistcoat together. Encourage them to make their own suggestions.

Help each child to choose one of the resources from your selection to join the sides of the front to the sides of the back. Once all the children have finished, explain that you would like them to join together the two halves of the front of the waistcoat. Invite them to choose a different method of joining from the one that they chose earlier.

Further idea
■ Using one of the photocopies as a template, draw around it on to thin fabric such as felt, and cut out the pieces. Invite the children to join the parts together as in the activity above.

Support and extension
For younger children, enlarge each of the photocopies to make them easier to cut out and join. Encourage older children to name and find the appropriate resources that they need.

Home links
Encourage parents and carers to ask their children to help with joining things together, such as sticking stamps on envelopes or stapling pieces of paper together.

Knowledge and understanding of the world

From new to old

Learning objective
To look closely at similarities, differences, patterns and change.

Group size
Four to six children.

What you need
Drawing and writing materials; the photocopiable sheet on page 120.

What to do
Look with the children at the page in the book that shows Missus Mac feeding a sheep. Ask whether they think that the sheep is old or young. Explain that it is a lamb because it still needs to be fed with a bottle, just as the children had to be when they were babies. Next, ask the children how they know that something is old. They may suggest that people look old when they have grey hair and wrinkles, or that old toys can be dirty and broken.

Give each child a copy of the photocopiable sheet. Encourage the children to describe each of the pictures. Explain that you would like them to think about how they could change each picture to make it look older. Taking each picture in turn, talk with the children about how they could 'age' the baby, seedling and lamb. Encourage them to draw on their existing knowledge – for example, trees are usually larger than saplings, older people are usually taller than small children, and so on.

Give the children the drawing materials and invite each child to draw in the empty space next to each picture an older person, a tree and a sheep respectively. Talk about what they are doing. When the children have completed their drawings, ask them to show their 'old' pictures and to talk about how they made them, comparing them with the original 'young' pictures.

Support and extension
For younger children, draw a baby's face on a flip chart or easel. Encourage them to tell you what to draw to make the face look old, such as glasses, wrinkles or grey hair. Ask older children to add more details to their pictures.

Home links
Invite parents and carers to show their children photographs of themselves as babies and to ask them to describe how they have changed physically.

Further idea
■ Look at the life cycle of frogs and butterflies, and discuss how they change as they grow and get older.

Physical development

Joined together

Learning objective
To show an awareness of space, of themselves and of others.

Group size
Four to six children.

What you need
Scarves or bands; large, empty floor space.

What to do
Show the children the picture in the book that shows children taking part in a three-legged race. Invite the children to get into pairs. Help them to loosely join their ankles together as in the picture and ask them to walk carefully around the large, empty floor space. Encourage them to try to work together to move forwards and to look for empty spaces big enough for the pair to move into.

Help the children to untie themselves. Talk with them about how they were joined together and had to help each other to move. Explain that you would like them to think of other ways to help each other to move around the room while joined together.

Give them a few minutes to do this, then ask them to show the rest of the group one way that they can be joined together and move.

Once all the pairs of children have demonstrated their moves, encourage each pair to copy some of the other pairs' ideas.

Support and extension
For younger children, provide suggestions of body parts that could be joined, saying, for example, 'Put your arms together' or 'Put your knees together'. Encourage older children to try to think about using as many body parts as possible, or to use more space, holding hands in the air or touching just fingertips.

Home links
Invite parents and carers to draw a person on a large piece of paper, such as old wallpaper or newspaper sheets taped together. Encourage them to call out two body parts, for example, 'Put your foot on the foot', and to ask their children to put that part of their body on to the appropriate part of the picture.

Further ideas
■ **Invite the children to choose two or three different methods of joining and to sequence them to make a pattern.**
■ **Challenge the children to find as many ways of linking identical body parts as possible, or to think of as many strange combinations as possible, such as hand to foot, foot to leg and so on.**

Physical development

Look both ways

Learning objective
To move with confidence, imagination and in safety.

Group size
Four or more children.

What you need
Large, empty space (preferably outdoors); strips of black and white card; sit-and-ride vehicles; playground chalk; timer.

What to do
In the middle of the large, empty space, put alternating black and white stripes on the floor to make a zebra crossing. Draw a simple road system on the floor using the playground chalk.

Look at the picture of Missus Mac helping some children to cross the road. Discuss with the children how they should cross a road safely. Choose a child to pretend to be Missus Mac and show them the pedestrian crossing that you have created. Divide the rest of the group into two. Ask half the children to pretend to be 'traffic' on the roads, and the remainder of the children to be 'pedestrians'.

Ask the 'traffic' to drive around the roads on the sit-and-ride vehicles, and the 'pedestrians' to walk beside the roads. Encourage the pedestrians to take it in turns to cross the road using the zebra crossing. Ask the drivers, if they see someone on the zebra crossing, to stop before the crossing and wait until the pedestrian has crossed safely.

Invite 'Missus Mac' to help the children to cross the road (not at the zebra crossing), while constantly looking and listening for traffic. Encourage 'Missus Mac' to hold her hand up to stop the traffic, as in the picture. Remind the children that they should only cross a real road when they are with their parent or carer, or a responsible adult that they know well.

Support and extension
For younger children, begin initially with the 'traffic' moving only in one direction around the space. Invite older children to have crossings at 'traffic-lights' too, asking one of the children to hold up coloured discs to show the colour of the traffic-lights.

Home links
Encourage parents and carers, when out with their children, to help them to recognize where a safe place to cross a road would be.

Further idea
■ Use fluorescent paint to make tabards and bands for the children to wear so that they can be seen by oncoming traffic (suitable for role-play only).

Creative development

Learning objective
To sing simple songs from memory.

Group size
Four or more children.

What you need
A variety of musical instruments; flip chart or easel and paper; marker pen.

Thank you

What to do

Look in the book at the pictures of Missus Mac on her last day. Explain to the children that usually, at a leaving assembly such as this one, children sing a few songs for the person who is leaving. Ask the children if they have ever been to a leaving assembly and invite any who have to tell the others what happened.

Explain to the children that you would like them to sing a few songs to say 'thank you' to some of the people that help them, whether in your setting or at home. Suggest some songs that they could sing. Encourage them to try to think of songs or nursery rhymes that are about people who help us, such as 'Miss Polly Had a Dolly' or 'The Wheels on the Bus' (Traditional). Ideally, these should be the children's favourite songs. Write the suggestions on the flip chart or easel.

Once you have a list of the songs, help the children to decide who is going to sing each song. Some of the children might want to sing by themselves, but some may prefer to sing with a friend or in a small group. Help the children to decide in which order the songs will be sung. Give them the opportunity to play musical instruments to accompany themselves and one another.

Allow the children ten minutes to work on the songs, then invite them to sing their songs in the order agreed. Encourage them to clap and congratulate the singers and musicians.

Try this activity one week in advance of when you would like the children to sing their songs in a special 'concert'. Then invite people who help around the setting, parents and carers to come to the 'concert'.

Further ideas
■ **Make programmes and invitations for the concert.**
■ **Encourage the children to make their own instruments.**

Support and extension

Younger children could sing their songs with an adult. Encourage older children to choose a song that perhaps only they know.

Home links

Invite parents and carers to come to the concert, telling them in advance about the book that you have been using for your theme.

Creative development

Tidy-up time

Learning objective
To explore shape, form and space in three dimensions.

Group size
Four to six children.

What you need
A selection of cardboard boxes of various sizes and shapes (try to include some with lids and some without); glue; glue spreaders; sticky tape; scissors; paint and other materials for decorating.

What to do
Talk about the picture where Missus Mac is helping the girl who is stuck to the glue on the floor. Invite the children to look closely at the picture and to suggest how the glue got on the floor (someone left the glue tube open). Explain to the children that you would like each of them to make something that can be put on a table to keep resources such as glue or pens tidy.

Show the children the various boxes that you have collected. Ask the children to suggest ways in which the boxes could be used to make the table tidy without gluing them. Ideas could include putting the boxes on top of each other, like a chest of drawers, or putting small boxes inside one large box.

Talk with each child about how they want to make their 'tidy boxes'. Encourage them to think about their resources and what they need. How many boxes will they require? How will they join them together?

Invite the children to make their tidy boxes, helping where necessary. Throughout, encourage them to talk about what they are doing. When they have completed their boxes, ask them to decorate them using paint or stickers, or anything that they want. Display the containers with pens or other resources for making pictures. Add labels explaining how each child made their models.

Support and extension
Invite younger children to just put the boxes side by side and staple or tape them together, or to put small boxes in the biggest one. Encourage older children to be more creative, for example, trying to make drawers or compartments in their boxes.

Home links
Ask parents and carers to help their children to decorate an empty tissue box or shoebox, which they can use for storing small things.

Further idea
■ Give each child a small piece of card (the size of a small address label) and ask them to write a label to stick on the side of their container to show what should be stored in it.

Role-play

Going swimming

Learning objective
To use their imagination in imaginative and role-play and stories.

Group size
Four to six children.

What you need
Large blue sheet or large blue roll of paper; desk; old swimming trunks and swimming costumes (one size or two larger than the children so that they can wear them on top of their everyday clothes); swimming floats; armbands; water safety posters; cash register; bath towels; money; book of tickets.

Further idea
■ **Invite the children to set up a restaurant for hungry swimmers to go to when they have changed.**

What to do
Tape the large blue sheet in a corner (or the edge) of the role-play area to make a 'swimming-pool'. Leave the armbands and swimming floats by its side. Opposite the pool, set up the desk with the cash register, money and book of tickets. Make another area into the changing room, where the children can put on the swimming costumes and use the towels to 'dry themselves'.

Look at the picture of Missus Mac at the swimming-pool and show the pool that you have created in the role-play area. Ask the children if they have ever been swimming and talk with them about their experiences. Explain that, normally, swimmers need to pay the receptionist and get changed before they can go swimming. Encourage the children to role-play paying their admission fee and getting changed. For hygiene reasons, swimsuits will have to be worn over everyday clothes.

Once in the 'water', the children could 'paddle' or lie on their stomachs or backs and pretend to swim. Tell them that, for safety reasons, there is to be no jumping or diving in the pool. Throughout, remind the children that they should never go swimming by themselves, and should only swim in a proper pool with an adult. At the end of the session, encourage the children to role-play drying themselves and getting dressed again.

Support and extension
Encourage younger children to draw on their own experiences of swimming with their parents or carers when appropriate. Invite older children to be more creative in their role-play, for example, carefully 'jumping into the water'.

Home links
Invite parents and carers to help their children to make posters encouraging children to behave safely near water, and ask the children to bring these in to show the rest of the group.

People Who Help

This book shows a wide range of people who help us, such as a teacher, waiter and vet, at work. It uses photographs of both adult helpers and children dressed up as those people. A glossary and index are included. While this book invites children to role-play helping one another, it can also encourage them to think about the specialist tools and uniforms that some people need for their jobs.

Using the book

Learning about glossaries, by using the glossary in the book, begins the Communication, language and literacy section. The children can read letters as they pretend to be librarians and readers looking for books. Included, too, is an activity that invites the children to make up simple riddles about people who help us.

In Mathematical development, the children pretend to be nurses and weigh and compare dolls. This section also invites the children to count teeth, as dentists might do, and to sort mail ready for posting into letter boxes.

The children are encouraged to think about cultural differences when they are asked to use chopsticks in a Personal, social and emotional development activity. They also play a simple 'Lotto' game, where they have to match special items of equipment and tools with the appropriate person.

The Knowledge and understanding of the world activities include talking about the variety of forms of technology that we can use to ask for help, and making a simple 'map' of the local area showing the buildings where we can find people who help us.

In Physical development, the children are invited to shape play dough to make plates of pretend food. They are also encouraged to think about how they clean their teeth by 'brushing' a giant set of pretend teeth.

In Creative development, using the book as a stimulus, the children each pretend to be a helping person and act out one part of their job while the other children try to guess who they are. The children also each make a tray for a waiter.

Role-play centres around a nursery where the children can pretend to look after 'babies'.

Communication, language and literacy

Keyboard, chalkboard

Learning objective
To show an understanding of how information can be found in non-fiction texts.

National Literacy Strategy
To read on sight the words from texts of appropriate difficulty; to learn new words from their reading.

Group size
Four children.

What you need
White A4 paper; marker pen.

What to do
Write each of the bold-type words from the glossary on separate sheets of paper. Read the book to the children, encouraging them to look at the pictures. As you read the words aloud, draw the children's attention to each of the highlighted words in bold type on the pages. Show them the glossary at the end of the book and explain that it tells readers more about some of the words that are found in the book, and that each of these words are things that people can use to help us. Read out one of the examples.

Give each child one of the sheets of paper with the individual words written on them and help them to read out their word. Then explain that you would like them to find, in the glossary of the book, the word that you gave them. Hold the book open on the glossary page so that all the children can see it. Invite the children, one at a time, to try to find their word on the page. Encourage them to check for the shape of the word and the sequence of letters in it.

Each time a word is found, help the children, as a group, to read its meaning. Track the words by pointing at them with your finger as you read to help the children. Continue until all the children have found their words.

Support and extension
Give younger children the same two or three words and, as a group, read the words and their meanings. Encourage older children to work more independently with their reading.

Home links
Invite parents and carers to find an information book that contains a glossary. Encourage them to help their children to read some of the words and their meanings.

Further idea
■ **Choose a simple non-fiction book that does not have a glossary and invite the children, as a group, to compile a glossary of some of the nouns, with the help of an adult acting as scribe.**

Communication, language and literacy

Where is the book?

Learning objectives
To interact with others, negotiating activities and taking turns in conversation; to name and sound letters of the alphabet.

National Literacy Strategy
To read letters that represent the sounds a–z.

Group size
Four children (two pairs).

What you need
The photocopiable sheet on page 121; picture of a book, mounted on to card, that will fit into one of the squares on the photocopiable sheet; pencil; A4 folder.

What to do
Show the children the picture of the librarian in the book and explain that librarians help people to find books and to borrow them. Then tell the children that librarians keep the library tidy by putting returned books on the shelves, matching the letters and numbers on the books with those on the shelves.

Invite one pair of children to be the librarians and give them the picture of the chosen book. Ask the other pair to be the readers, and give them the pencil. Give each pair a copy of the photocopiable sheet. Place the A4 folder in between the pairs to hide the librarians' sheet from the readers.

Ask the librarians to quietly put the book picture on to one of the letter squares on their sheet, without saying where it is. Explain to them that the book must stay on the same square until the game ends.

Invite the readers to ask the librarians where the book is hidden by calling out one of the letters on the photocopiable sheet, for example, 'Is the book on the "c"?'. The librarians

must answer truthfully 'yes' or 'no'. If the answer is 'no', the readers can cross out the letter that they said with the pencil. The readers then name another letter for the librarians to check. If the readers guess correctly, the readers and librarians can swap places, and the new librarians choose a new place to put the book on.

Support and extension
For younger children, mask out some of the letters and re-photocopy the sheet. Give older children sheets with more letters on them.

Home links
Give each child three letters to take home and read to their parents or carers.

Further idea
■ **Choose five letters and write out each one on a separate sheet of A1 paper. Spread the letters out on the floor of a large, empty space. Call them out one at a time and challenge the children to go and stand on the correct letter.**

Communication, language and literacy

I wear a yellow hat

Learning objective
To enjoy listening to and using spoken and written language, and readily turn to it in their play and learning.

National Literacy Strategy
To use experience of stories, poems and simple recounts as a basis for independent writing, such as retelling, substitution, extension, and through shared composition with adults.

Group size
Four to six children.

What you need
The photocopiable sheet on page 107.

What to do
Talk about the helpers in the book, such as the firefighter, the special clothes that they wear (a yellow hat) and the jobs that they do (putting out fires).

Tell the children that you are going to read them a riddle about someone who helps us. Explain that it tells us about what they wear or do, but it does not tell us who they are. Invite the children to tell you, after you have read the first riddle from the photocopiable sheet, which person they think the helper might be. Is it a police officer, a nurse or a firefighter? Read the remaining riddles and invite the children to say whom each describes.

Explain to the children that you would like each of them to think of a riddle about someone who helps us. Invite each child to think of a helping person, but not to say who it is. Next, encourage the children to think of three or four things that that person might use, or of what they do in their job. Ask each child to say their riddle, without saying which person it is about, and invite the other children to guess who it is.

Support and extension
Ask younger children to think of one thing that the helper wears and one thing that they do. Give older children a piece of paper entitled 'Who am I?' each and encourage them to write their rhyme on it at their own level of writing, possibly using an adult as a scribe.

Home links
Invite the children to take their riddles home to their parents and carers for them to guess who they are about.

Further idea
■ Invite each child to 'write' (at whatever level they are able to) a story about the person in their riddle.

How heavy is the baby?

Learning objective
To use language such as 'greater', 'smaller', 'heavier' or 'lighter' to compare two quantities.

National Numeracy Strategy
To use language such as 'heavier' or 'lighter' to compare two quantities.

Group size
Four to six children.

What you need
Six or seven different-sized dolls; balance scales, large enough to hold the dolls; one 'chart' for each doll, with spaces to write a doll's name, birth date and birth weight; small wooden bricks (all the same size and shape).

What to do
Look in the book at the picture of the nurse with the baby in the hospital. Talk with the children about how babies need to be weighed and measured so that doctors, nurses and midwives can make sure that they are growing and developing properly.

Next, tell the children that you would like them to pretend to be nurses and healthcare workers, and to weigh some babies to find out which ones are the heaviest and which ones are the lightest.

Show the children the largest doll. Put the doll on one side of the scales. Invite the children to help you to put some wooden blocks on the other pan until the weights balance. Encourage them to say whether the doll or the blocks are heavier or lighter each time a block is added.

Fill in one of the charts with a name for the doll, a birth date (it could be the same as one of the children's) and how many blocks it equals. Invite the children to take it in turns to guess how many blocks they think the doll will weigh, and to compare the doll with one already weighed to say whether they think it is heavier or lighter. The children could also draw a picture of each doll on its weight chart.

Support and extension
Encourage younger children to work as a group. Invite older children to begin to use standard measures to weigh the dolls.

Home links
Invite parents and carers to help their children to compare three of their soft toys and to decide which weighs the most and which weighs the least.

Further ideas
■ **Use coloured sand and small plastic tubs to make 'baby food' to feed the dolls. Invite the children to make more food for the bigger babies and smaller 'meals' for the tiny babies.**
■ **Show the children the picture of the vet on the poster depicting people who help us. Talk about why the vet might need a set of scales and repeat the activity above using soft-toy animals instead of dolls.**

Mathematical development

Learning objective
To count reliably up to ten everyday objects.

National Numeracy Strategy
To begin to record numbers, initially by making marks, progressing to simple tallying and writing numerals.

Group size
Four to six children.

What you need
The photocopiable sheet on page 122; pencils; list of the things that a dentist might do to people's teeth, such as drilling, filling, filing, capping and cleaning; erasers.

What to do
With the children, look in the book at the picture of the dentist checking the teeth of the patient. Ask them if they have ever been to the dentist's. If so, invite them to talk about what happened there.

Describe to the children how the dentist counts the patient's teeth to make sure that they are all there and to see if they need anything doing to them.

Give each child a copy of the photocopiable sheet and a pencil. Tell them that you are going to say some jobs that a dentist might do and a number, for example, 'One tooth needs filling'. Explain to the children that when you do this, you would like each of them to draw a line across that number of teeth (one line per tooth) on their sheet (any of the teeth, top or bottom).

Say the things that some teeth might need doing, using the list that you have written as a stimulus, and pausing after each job to allow the children to cross off the teeth on their sheets. Decide to stop when you have reached a total of ten teeth or less, then invite the children to count how many of the teeth needed work by counting the lines that they marked on them.

Ten teeth

Help the children to rub out all the marks so that they can try again, or give them new sheets. Finally, let them take turns to call out jobs that teeth need doing.

Support and extension
For younger children, initially suggest jobs that only up to five teeth in total need doing. Encourage older children to try to write the appropriate numeral by the side of the mouth.

Home links
Invite parents and carers to make a simple list of five objects that they have more than one of in their kitchen cupboards. Encourage them to give the list to their children and to help them to count the objects and 'write' down next to each item the appropriate number.

Further idea
■ **Invite the children to make teeth from play dough and to count them.**

Sorted!

Learning objective
To recognize numerals 1 to 9.

National Numeracy Strategy
To recognize numerals 1 to 9.

Group size
Four to six children.

What you need
Ten cardboard boxes of different sizes and shapes; glue; sticky tape; paint; scissors; 27 blank envelopes in a variety of sizes and colours; nine large paper bags; nine sheets of white A4 paper; marker pen.

What to do
Write numbers from 1 to 9 on the bags, sheets of white paper and envelopes (there will be three envelopes for each number).

Show the children the picture in the book of the postal worker sorting letters. Explain how the sorting machine 'reads' the postcodes at the bottom of the addresses on the letters and envelopes and then sorts and matches them. Tell the children that you would like them to pretend to be postal workers sorting the mail.

Invite the children to make an envelope sorting machine. Show them the envelopes and their numbers and explain that they first need to be collected ready for sorting. Help the children to choose a large box for this part of the sorting machine. Explain that once the letters are in the machine, they need to be sorted ready for putting into bags for the postal workers to deliver. Ask the children to put one number on each of the remaining boxes, so that they are

numbered 1 to 9. Once all the boxes have been labelled, help the children to put them into numerical order and to tape them together. The finished sorting machine could be painted, but wait for the paint to dry before using it!

Invite the children to put the envelopes into the machine and to sort them into the individually-numbered boxes. Encourage them to take it in turns to pretend to be postal workers and put the sorted letters into the appropriately-numbered paper bags before 'delivering' them.

Support and extension
With younger children, initially only use numbers from 1 to 5. With older children, include the numbers 0 and 10.

Home links
Encourage parents and carers to help their children to find and read numbers around the house on remote controls or displays on clocks and microwave ovens.

Further ideas
■ **Make letter boxes, with numbers, for the postal workers to deliver the letters to.**
■ **Make a shape sorting machine for wrapped parcels.**

Personal, social and emotional development

Chinese chopsticks

Learning objective
To understand that people have different needs and cultures that need to be treated with respect.

Group size
Four to six children.

What you need
Large plastic bowl; a plastic fork, pair of chopsticks and small plastic bowl for each child; small plastic shapes or animals; cooked, cold noodles or spaghetti, or pieces of string.

What to do
Show the children the picture in the book of the waiter in the Chinese restaurant and the child holding the tray. Ask them to compare the table settings in both pictures. Some of the children may notice that there are chopsticks on one table, and knives and forks on the other.

Explain that, traditionally, Chinese food is eaten with chopsticks. Give each child a set of chopsticks and show them how to use them. (Hold both chopsticks, one below the other, in one hand. The lower chopstick never moves. The top chopstick is held between the index and middle fingers and moves up and down in a pincer-like movement to pick up food.) Help the children to use them.

In the large bowl, mix up the noodles and the small plastic shapes or animals. Give each child a fork, a set of chopsticks and a small bowl. Encourage the children to take it in turns, using the forks, to get a small animal or shape from the large bowl and put it in their small bowls. Continue until there are no shapes left in the bowl. Put all the shapes back into the large bowl and repeat using the chopsticks instead. Talk with the children about how chopsticks are ideal for eating Chinese food, but not so good for eating a roast dinner, and that knives and forks are good for cutting potatoes and meat, but not so useful for picking up rice and noodles!

Support and extension
For younger children, use larger shapes and provide extra help with the chopsticks. For older children, provide more noodles and fewer shapes.

Home links
Invite parents and carers to provide a small plate of food from another country for all the children to share in your setting.

Further idea
■ **Have a table with display food, pictures of hands, chopsticks, knives, and forks. Encourage the children to match each food with how it would normally be eaten.**

Personal, social and emotional development

Help 'Lotto'

Learning objective
To maintain attention, concentrate and sit quietly when appropriate.

Group size
Four children.

What you need
The photocopiable sheet on page 123; card; scissors.

What to do

Make four copies of the photocopiable sheet on to card, laminate the sheets and cut each one in half horizontally, separating the two sets of pictures. Put to one side the top halves of the sheets (pictures of people who help us) to make 'Lotto' base boards, then cut out the six pictures from the lower half of each photocopy.

Explain to the children that you would like them to play a game where they have to match some special clothes and equipment with the correct owner. Give each child a base board and show the children the cut-up pictures. Check that they all understand each of the pictures. Talk about which person, on the base board, would use each of the items on the pictures, such as the doctor and their stethoscope, referring to the appropriate pages in the book.

Spread the pictures face down in the middle of the four players. Choose one child to start the game. Invite them to select one of the pictures, turn it over

and say what it shows and who would use the item. If they are right, ask them to place the picture on top of the corresponding person. Then the next child has their turn.

If a picture cannot be placed on a board because the matching space has already been filled, it must be turned face down again and put back in the middle of the players. Play until all the children have covered all the spaces on their 'Lotto' boards. Remind them to sit quietly while they wait for their turn.

Support and extension

For younger children, play until one child has covered all the people on their base board with the correct items. Invite older children to roll a dice before turning over a picture. If a player rolls a 1, they miss a turn and the next ◆ player has their turn.

Home links

Suggest that parents and carers play games such as 'Snakes and ladders' or 'Ludo' with their children.

Further idea
■ Invite the children to make up their own versions of the game, using their own illustrations.

Knowledge and understanding of the world

Keep in touch

Learning objective
To find out about and identify the uses of everyday technology.

Group size
Four to six children.

What you need
Sheets of pale A5 paper; a piece of card the width of three sheets of A5 paper for each child; thin ribbon; scissors; hole-punch; hole-reinforcing rings; ruler; drawing and writing materials.

What to do
On the long pieces of card, draw two vertical lines to divide each piece of card into three equal parts (A5 size).

Read the book and explore the pictures, such as the police officer and their walkie-talkie, or the vet talking to the cat's owners. Ask the children to suggest ways that they could ask for help, such as writing a note, using a telephone or just asking another person, 'Please, can you help me?'.

Give each child one of the long pieces of card, three sheets of A5 paper and some drawing and writing materials. Ask them to draw a picture of themselves on the left-hand side of the piece of card. Then invite them to draw a picture of someone that they could ask for help, such as a family member or doctor, on the right-hand side of the piece of card. Finally, tell them to draw, on each of the three sheets of A5 paper, one thing that they could use to ask for help, as discussed earlier.

Once the children have finished their pictures, punch two holes through the top of each one and the top of the middle section of each piece of card. Strengthen the holes with reinforcing rings, and thread lengths of ribbon through them. With the card at the back, knot the ends together behind it. Show the children how they can 'flip' the pictures backwards and forwards, and ask them to describe what could be happening in them, such as 'I'm ringing Gran'.

Child's picture　　**Ribbon**　　**Holes made using hole-punch**

Method of communication　　**Picture of a person who helps us**

Support and extension
Invite younger children to think of just two ways to ask for help. Encourage older children to think of more ideas, or to try to label their pictures.

Home links
Invite parents and carers to show their children how to use a telephone in an emergency, explaining that they should only call emergency services if there *is* an emergency.

Further idea
■ **Make 'telephones' from old cardboard boxes, adding to them stickers with numbers.**

Knowledge and understanding of the world

In your local area

Learning objective
To observe, find out about and identify features in the place they live.

Group size
Four to six children.

What you need
Three or four sheets of white A1 paper; drawing and writing materials.

What to do
Two or three days in advance, walk around your local area without the children and make a list of all the buildings where the children could find people to help them, such as libraries, shops and surgeries. If necessary, arrange extra adult help for the activity.

Use the book to invite the children to name as many people who help us as possible and the places where they can be found. Explain that you would like to take them for a short walk around your local area and that, as you do so, you would like them to look for places where they could find people who could help them, for example, police stations or shops. Walk the children around the route that you planned earlier, encouraging them to

look for buildings that might have helpful people inside them.

Back in your setting, invite the children to make a simple map with pictures of the buildings that they saw on the walk. Divide the children into pairs. Give each pair a sheet of A1 paper and some drawing and writing materials, and invite them to draw a picture of your setting in the middle of the paper. Then encourage them to draw around it pictures of the local buildings where they can find helpful people. (These do not have to be in the same positions on the paper as in reality!) Finally, ask the children to draw, next to each building, a picture of the helpful people that they can find there. They can also draw 'roads' from the setting to each of the buildings.

Support and extension
Encourage younger children to draw fewer, larger pictures. Invite older children to label their pictures.

Home links
Ask parents and carers to look out with their children for people who help us when they are travelling around their local area.

Further idea
■ **Use the drawings as a stimulus to make model buildings from small plastic bricks or old cardboard boxes.**

Physical development

At the restaurant

Learning objective
To handle tools and malleable materials safely and with increasing control.

Group size
Four to six children.

What you need
Books about food from different cultures, such as *Evening Meals Around the World* by Gill Munton (Hodder Wayland), or empty food packets and boxes showing the box contents and any serving suggestions; play dough in a variety of 'food' colours, such as green, orange, red, yellow and brown; tools to use with the play dough for cutting and mark-making; paper plates.

What to do
With the children, look in the book at the picture of the waiter in the Chinese restaurant and at the child pretending to look after some toy animals in a pretend restaurant.

Explain to the children that a waiter brings food to customers' tables in a restaurant and knows about the different food available. Tell them that many types of food that we like were originally made in a different country – for example, pizza and pasta in Italy, curries in India and so on. Look with the children at some of the pictures of food from around the world in the books that you have collected and, as you do so, discuss the colours, shapes and, where appropriate, the textures of the foods.

Give the children the play dough and tools and invite them to make food from another country. Encourage them to talk about the food that they are making and how they can shape the dough. As they work, invite them to use the tools and their hands to try to

create the effect that they want. For example, they could roll dough on the table to make noodles, or press dough through a sieve and cut the dough that comes out of the holes into small pieces to make 'rice'.

Finally, ask the children to place their pretend food on paper plates and display them on a table along with the books about multicultural food.

Support and extension
Provide younger children with extra support when shaping the play dough. Encourage older children to experiment more with how they can shape the dough.

Home links
Invite parents and carers to involve their children in shaping soft sweets, such as peppermint creams, or in using shaped cutters to make a variety of biscuits and sandwiches.

Further idea
■ Make 'menus' by writing on sheets of A4 card the names of the foods that the children have made. Encourage them to take it in turns to 'wait' on the other children and take their orders from the menu.

Let's brush our teeth!

Learning objective
To recognize the importance of keeping healthy and those things which contribute to this.

Group size
Four children.

What you need
Aprons; thick cardboard; scissors; glue; 20 small, identical, clean plastic pots; large paintbrushes; thick paint mixed with PVA glue.

What to do
Arrange ten of the pots, with the open top face down, in a horseshoe shape on a piece of thick cardboard so that the rims of the pots touch one another, and glue them on the board. Repeat on a separate piece of cardboard for the other ten pots. The aim is to replicate (although with fewer teeth!) the jaw of a human being.

With the children, look in the book at the picture of the dentist checking the patient's teeth and ask them to tell you why we go to the dentist's and what happens there. Then invite the children to discuss how they can look after their teeth. Suggestions could include not eating sweets and brushing their teeth twice a day. Explain that brushing our teeth cleans away the bits of food left over from our meals or snacks, and helps to keep them healthy.

Encourage the children to tell you how they should brush their teeth, then show them the large sets of 'teeth' that you have created. Give one of the children a large paintbrush and ask them to brush the pretend teeth as they would brush their own teeth. Check that the child is brushing the teeth properly, including the top, back

and sides. Then explain to the children that you would like them to 'brush' the pretend teeth using paint mixed with PVA glue as toothpaste. Give each child a paintbrush.

As the children 'brush' the teeth, encourage them to paint all the areas and to move their brushes slowly backwards and forwards or in circles. End the activity when all the teeth are completely covered with paint.

Support and extension
Give younger children the largest brushes that you can find. Encourage older children to use smaller brushes.

Home links
Ask parents and carers to tell their children which toothpaste they use. Which is the most popular toothpaste?

Further idea
■ Put a little air into pairs of rubber gloves and tightly fasten them around the children's wrists with elastic bands. Put some 'dirt' (blue or green paint) on to the gloves and encourage the children to wash their 'hands' with soap and water.

Creative development

Today, I am...

Learning objective
To express and communicate their ideas using mime.

Group size
Four or more children.

What you need
Just the children.

What to do
With the children, look at each of the pictures in the book and talk about what is happening. Encourage them to look particularly at how the person who helps in the picture is helping someone else.

Invite the children to assist you in choosing three of the people who help us from the book. Name one of them and ask the children to tell you something that that person does for their job – for example, a firefighter drives a fire engine, climbs ladders and holds a water hose. Encourage some of the children to show the other children how that person does those activities. Repeat this for the other two people that you selected.

Next, tell the children that you would like them, one at a time, to choose a person who helps us and to think of one thing that they do every day for

their job. Explain that you want each child to demonstrate to the others the action that they thought of, but not to say either what the action is or who they are pretending to be.

Begin the activity yourself by showing the children the action appropriate to the person that you have chosen to be. Encourage them to guess what you are doing and who you are pretending to be. Then invite each child, in turn, to mime someone being helpful, for the others to try to guess who it is. Continue until everyone has had a turn.

Support and extension
For younger children, choose just one person from the book for them to pretend to be. Encourage them to think of as many different actions as possible for that person to do. Ask older children to each try to choose a different person.

Home links
Invite parents and carers to think of a person who helps us. Ask them to give clues to the occupation of that person for their children to try to guess who they are.

Further idea
■ **Do a group mime where three or four children try to re-create a scene where one of them is helping someone else.**

Learning objective
To use their imagination in art and design.

Group size
Four to six children.

What you need
Squares and rectangles of thick card (at least A4 size) in a variety of colours; scissors; materials for decorating, such as paints, stickers and scraps of fabric and paper; sticky tape; small plastic cups and plates; scissors; glue; glue spreaders.

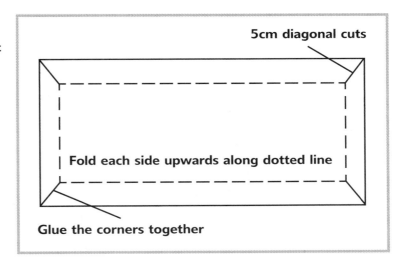

5cm diagonal cuts

Fold each side upwards along dotted line

Glue the corners together

What to do
Read the book to the children and show them the picture of the child pretending to be a waiter. Talk with them about what the tray is used for and how it helps the waiter to carry lots of things at a time. Look closely with the children at the shape of the tray. Explain that it needs to be flat so that objects can balance easily on top of it, and that sometimes trays have sides to prevents things from falling off.

Next, tell the children that you would like them to each make a tray of their own. Invite each child to choose a piece of card. Help them to make a five-centimetre diagonal cut at each corner of the card. Show them how to turn their card into a tray by folding each side upwards to form the sides of the tray, then securing the corners by gluing each cut end on to the adjacent one (see diagram above).

Encourage the children to decorate their trays using the paint or collage materials. Remind them that the decorations need to be kept as flat as possible to prevent anything on top of the tray from falling over when the tray is carried. Once the trays are finished, make a watery solution of glue and brush them with it to protect them.

Invite the children to test their trays by putting some of the plastic cups and plates on them before trying to carefully carry them around the room.

Support and extension
Invite younger children to each decorate a shallow cardboard box to make a tray. Encourage older children to work more independently to make their trays.

Home links
Draw carefully around each child's tray on to a piece of paper. Cut out the outline and give each to the appropriate child. Invite parents and carers to help their children to design a picture to fit on to their tray.

Further idea
■ **Encourage the children to make cups and plates from play dough, which they can carry on their trays.**

■ **Role-play**

Looking after baby

Learning objective
To be sensitive to the needs, views and feelings of others.

Group size
Four to six children.

What you need
A small doll for each child (male and female, and with a variety of skin tones); an open-top box for each child; old small sheets and blankets; accessories for the dolls, such as old babies' bottles, empty boxes of baby food, nappies, pretend thermometers and doctor's equipment; tabards for the 'doctors' and 'nurses'; sheets of A4 paper; drawing and writing materials.

What to do
With the children, look in the book at the picture of the nurse with the baby. Explain to them that you have turned the role-play area into a nursery. Show them the dolls and invite them to pretend to look after them.

Ask the children if any of them have a younger brother or sister at home. Invite those children to tell the rest of the group about some of the things that parents or carers need to do for a baby, such as feeding them, changing them, weighing them and letting them sleep. Talk with the children about what happens in a hospital to a new baby, such as measuring them and giving them a bath.

Encourage each child, initially, to think of a name for their baby and to write it on a sheet of paper. Then ask them to also write on the paper how heavy the baby is. (Either use this as a mathematical activity, or encourage the children to 'write' some numbers on their sheets.) Invite the children to 'update' their records regularly. As the activity progresses, the children can talk about their babies' needs, such as toys to play with, going to the doctor's when they are ill and so on. Encourage the children to be quiet when the babies are asleep.

Support and extension
Encourage younger children to work together to look after the babies. Invite older children to look after two babies at a time each.

Home links
Suggest to parents and carers that they ask their children to help them to look after younger siblings, pets or teddies (where appropriate).

Further ideas
■ Make a 'rota' with the names of the children to show who can be in the nursery looking after the babies.
■ Using as a stimulus the picture of the vet on the poster showing people who help us, turn the nursery into a veterinary centre or animal sanctuary. Provide soft-toy animals and encourage the children to 'look after' them.

Chapter 5

In the City

This colourful book shows places in a city at different times of the day. It begins with people arriving at work in the morning and ends with them going home in the evening. It can help to remind children of the helping people that they might have met on trips to a city. It also introduces them to people who make our environment a nicer place, such as gardeners.

Using the book

The Communication, language and literacy activities begin by encouraging the children to experiment with saying words and sounds from the book in different ways. The children then sing a song that requires them to think about people who help us and the objects and equipment that they use. The children also make simple pictorial stories about one of the characters in the book.

A game of addition and subtraction where the children have to 'plant' flowers in pots starts the Mathematical development section. Then the children take it in turns to be customers and a shop assistant to develop their counting skills. Using small-world equipment, the children create a park and describe where to put each of the park visitors.

The Personal, social and emotional development activities encourage the children to think about what is right and what is wrong, and to select their own resources to make 3-D buildings.

In the Knowledge and understanding of the world activities, the children draw pictures of their setting and of someone who helps to keep it tidy and clean. They also make simple lift-the-flap books revealing animals or birds.

In Physical development, the children move as different people who help us would do, and a large, empty floor space is turned into a park where they pretend to be park keepers, picking up litter and putting it in bins.

In Creative development, the children make tool boxes and tools, and re-create daytime and night-time noises using instruments and their voices.

In the role-play activity, the children create a park, trying to make it as realistic as possible by using features, sounds and smells.

Communication, language and literacy

Flap words

Learning objective
To explore and experiment with sounds, words and texts.

National Literacy Strategy
To hear and identify initial sounds in words.

Group size
Four or more children.

What you need
Just the children.

What to do

Read the book to the children and choose one of the flaps that 'hides' a person helping, for example, the one with the bus door and 'Whose blue bus is this?' written on it. Hold the book so that the children can see the words. Re-read the words on the flap out loud, pointing to each word as you do so. Encourage the children to repeat the words after you.

Re-read the question 'Whose blue bus is this?' differently from how you read it before, for example, very slowly. Invite the children to join in with you as you say the words. Explain to them that you are going to say one of the words on the page and that you would like them to listen carefully to it and to think about the sound that it begins with, but not to say what it is. Read one of the words from the question in your normal reading voice. Encourage the children to suggest another way that the word can be read, such as fast or quietly. Choose one of the children's suggestions and re-read the word in that way, then invite the children to tell you what sound they think that word begins with.

Repeat each of the other words, with the children saying them in different ways, then try to decide which sound each word begins with. Encourage the children to look at the picture of the person who says the words and to say the words as that person would say them – for example, the shop assistant may have a squeaky voice, or the gardener may have a deep voice.

Support and extension

Invite younger children to just say the words in different ways. Encourage older children to tell you the sound that each word ends with, too.

Home links

Encourage parents and carers to invite their children to experiment with how they say well-known nursery rhymes and stories by saying them slowly or whispering them.

Further idea
■ Invite each child to think of a word (types of food are popular!) and suggest to the other children how they would like it said. Encourage the children to repeat the word.

Communication, language and literacy

Helpful people

Learning objective
To sustain attentive listening, responding to what they have heard.

National Literacy Strategy
To re-read and recite stories and rhymes with predictable and repeated patterns, and experiment with similar rhymes and stories.

Group size
Four or more children.

What you need
The photocopiable sheet on page 110.

What to do
Read the book to the children and, as you do so, talk with them about the people and how they can help us, such as the gardener planting flowers or the builder on the building site. Show the children the pages again for each of the helping people (bus driver, builder, shop assistant and gardener) and encourage them to look at any special clothes or equipment that they might be wearing or using for their job, such as the safety hat, hammer, till and overalls.

Explain to the children that you are going to teach them a new song. Tell them that you are going to read out some words and that you would like them to listen carefully. Read the words on the photocopiable sheet. Re-read them, inviting the children to join in if they think that they know the words. Repeat one more time, singing the words to the music.

Choose one of the children to help you. Begin by singing the first question in the song. Encourage the children to join in with you, then invite the child that you chose to answer the question.

Encourage the children to suggest another object that a helping person in the book might use, such as a spanner. Sing the song again, changing the words as appropriate, with a different child giving the answer. Continue for as long as you wish, with the children suggesting new objects and people that they could be linked to.

Support and extension
Encourage younger children to sing as a group both the questions and the answers. Invite older children to suggest helping people and items that they use which are not mentioned in the book, for example, a doctor and their stethoscope.

Home links
Invite the children to take a copy of the song home to share with their parents or carers.

Further idea
■ Make a collection of songs and stories on the theme of people who help us that have repetitions, such as 'The Wheels on the Bus' (Traditional).

Communication, language and literacy

What did they do?

Learning objective
To show an understanding of the elements of stories, such as main character, sequence of events and openings.

National Literacy Strategy
To understand how story-book language works and to use some formal elements when retelling stories.

Group size
Four to six children.

What you need
The photocopiable sheet on page 105; A4 paper; drawing and writing materials.

What to do
Read the book to the children and talk about how each of the people in the pictures helps us. Explain to the children that some of the people and animals in the book are drawn on more than one page. For example, the builder gets off the bus with his hard hat and tool bag in his hands, and then on the next double page is working on the building site, with his hard hat on his head. Look at each of the pages in turn and encourage the children to find the people and animals that can be seen in more than one place in the book.

Explain to the children that you are going to read a story that is about the shop assistant in the book. Read the photocopiable sheet, then talk with the children about the events in the story and the order in which they happened.

Give each child four sheets of paper and drawing and writing materials. Tell them that you would like them to choose one helper from the book and to 'write' a story about what happens to them. The story could be about where the helping person goes, or who they help, for example, the builder who is going to the building site. Encourage the children to talk about which person they will 'write' about and to think of four things that could happen to them.

Ask the children to draw the first thing that happens in their story on one sheet of paper, then to draw each of the remaining events of their story on a separate sheet of paper. Once the children have finished, invite them to share their stories with the rest of the group by 'reading' the pictures in sequence.

Support and extension
Encourage younger children to think of just three events in their story. Invite older children to add captions to their pictures.

Home links
Ask parents and carers to encourage their children to retell favourite stories at home.

Further idea
■ Invite the children to decorate cardboard tubes with the characters from their stories and to use these 'puppets' for retelling their stories.

Plant the flowers

Learning objective
To begin to relate addition to combining two groups and subtraction to 'taking away'.

National Numeracy Strategy
To begin to relate addition to combining two groups of objects, counting all the objects; to begin to relate subtraction to 'taking away' and counting how many are left.

Group size
Four children.

What you need
The photocopiable sheet on page 124; dice; 40 small flower shapes; four different-coloured counters; four flowerpot-shaped pieces of card, each with spaces for ten flower shapes drawn on them.

What to do
Show the children the gardener in the book. Discuss how gardeners help us by making where we live look attractive and colourful. Invite the children to play a 'planting game' with you.

Put the flower shapes in the middle of the children. Show the group a copy of the base board on the photocopiable sheet and give each child a card flowerpot. Explain to the children that they are going to take turns to throw the dice. When they land on a 'plus', they must add flowers from the central pile to their pot (equal to the number showing on the dice), and if they land on a 'minus', they must take flowers from their pot and put them back in the middle.

Invite each child to take a counter and put it on the 'Start' petal, then choose one child to begin. Each turn, the player rolls the dice and moves their counter a number of spaces equal to the number showing on the dice.

Encourage them to say what is written on the square that they land on, and help them to take the appropriate action. Invite them to count the number of flowers that they have on their pot and the quantity that they are adding or removing. A maximum of ten flowers can be added to a pot. When a pot is full, play passes to the next child. If a child has no flowers on their pot and they land on a minus, the next child has a turn. Continue until all the children reach the 'Finish' petal.

Support and extension
Give younger children flowerpots with space for just five flowers. Give older children two flowerpots each.

Home links
Invite parents and carers to encourage their children to add groups of objects such as fruit or tins.

Further idea
■ **Provide a flowering plant. Help the children to keep a chart showing the number of flowers on it each day.**

Learning objective
To begin to use the vocabulary involved in adding and subtracting.

National Numeracy Strategy
To begin to relate addition to counting on and subtraction to 'taking away'.

Group size
Four to six children.

What you need
A basket for each child; wide selection of pretend food; ten pieces of card; marker pen; till; cardboard box painted to look like a shop scanner.

Ten items only

What to do
On each of the pieces of card, write 'items only', leaving a space before 'items'. In this space, write a number from 1 to 10 on each card.

Show the children the picture of the shop assistant using the till in the book. Explain that you would like them to take it in turns to be a shop assistant and customers. Invite one of the children to be the till assistant and give them the cards labelled with the numbers of items. Give each of the other children a basket and invite them to be 'customers'.

Ask the shop assistant to choose one of the cards to display next to the till where the customers can see it. Help the children to read the words on the card. Tell them that you would like them to put that number of items in their baskets. Once each of the children has filled their basket with the appropriate number of items, invite them to give the items, one at a time, to the shop assistant for them to 'scan' by pulling it slowly over the top of the scanner. Encourage the children to count the items as they are scanned, then to put them back into their own baskets.

Ask a different child to be the till assistant and invite them to change the card with the number of items allowed on it.

Encourage the customers to change the number of items in their baskets to match the new quantity, and invite them to say whether they are adding items to their baskets or taking some away. Repeat until each child has had the opportunity to be the shop assistant.

Support and extension
With younger children, use numbers to 5. With older children, change the cards for each customer.

Home links
Encourage parents and carers to help their children to count the items that they have bought when going shopping for just a few small items.

Further idea
■ Repeat the activity above, inviting the children to pay one coin for each item in their baskets.

Where are they?

Learning objective
To use everyday words to describe position.

National Numeracy Strategy
To use everyday words to describe position, direction and movement.

Group size
Four to six children.

What you need
Green paper for the grass; white A4 paper; drawing and writing materials; small-world equipment (two or three figures, a bench, a tree and a dog).

What to do
Read the book to the children and show them the pages of the park, then ask them to help you to set up the small-world equipment to make a similar scene. Invite the children, one at a time, to move the figures around. Encourage them to say where the figures are in relation to each other and to the objects that are in the 'park' – for example, 'The gardener is by the bench' or 'The dog is behind the tree'.

Encourage each of the children to think of two different places, then of positional words that they could use when moving the small-world figures to those places. Give each child a sheet of white paper and some drawing and writing materials. Ask them to say one word that indicates the position of an object, such as 'under', and help them to write that word on their sheet. Next, tell them that you would like them to draw on their sheet a picture that shows something in the position indicated by the word that is on their paper. Encourage them to draw all the relevant objects. For the dog to be in the tree, for example, they would need to draw the tree as well as the dog. Continue until each of the children has tried this two or three times for different positional words and objects.

Once the children have completed their pictures, invite them to swap drawings and to try to describe what they can see in them.

Support and extension
For younger children, omit the drawing activity. Encourage older children to draw a more detailed picture and invite them to show several things in different positions.

Home links
Encourage parents and carers to make up some silly instructions for their children to act out (making sure that they stay safe), for example, 'Put your elbow on your hand' or 'Put one foot on your knee'.

Further idea
■ Ask the children to re-create the scenes from the book by themselves.

Personal, social and emotional development

Be careful

Learning objective
To understand what is right, what is wrong and why.

Group size
Four or more children.

What you need
Large, empty floor space.

What to do
Read the book to the children and draw their attention to the pictures, especially the helping people. Invite the children to describe how each of these can help us – for example, the builder makes useful places for us to visit, such as shops. Look again at the pictures, starting with the pages that show the bus. Talk with the children about how the people are crossing the road and invite them to tell you how and when they should cross the road. Encourage them to think of as many different things as possible that people are doing that will keep them safe, or that involve helping another person. Repeat with each of the other pictures. Ideas might include staying away from building sites and using litter bins when walking in the park. Next, invite the children to think of things that are not helpful (from looking at the pictures), such as dropping litter on the ground.

Sit the children in the middle of a large, empty floor space. Explain that you are going to say some of the things that you have been talking about. If you mention something good, the children have to stay sitting down. If you say something that is not helpful, such as not looking before you cross the road, the children have to run to one side of the room (or put their arms in the air). After they have run, encourage them to sit back in the centre of the room.

Support and extension
For younger children, focus on the things that they should do (the 'right' things). Encourage older children to suggest reasons why they should and should not do certain things.

Home links
Encourage the children to tell their parents or carers three things that they must do at home, such as put their toys away, and the reasons why they should do it.

Further idea
■ **Invite the children to make up mimes showing good things to do, using the book as a stimulus.**

Personal, social and emotional development

Busy builders

Learning objective
To select and use activities and resources independently.

Group size
Four to six children.

What you need
Photographs of the children; variety of construction materials, such as small wooden or plastic bricks, large bricks and materials for making box models; ten sheets of A5 card, each with a picture of a building that could be made from the construction materials that you have selected; at least 20 pieces of card, each the size of a quarter of a sheet of A4 and with a picture or photograph of a resource that the children might need; notice-board at the children's height; Blu-Tack.

What to do
At the top of the notice-board, leave space for the children's photographs. Use Blu-Tack to stick the pictures of the buildings underneath. At the bottom of the board, place the pictures of resources.

Look at the picture of the builder in the book and talk about how he helps people. Invite the children to suggest what he could be building, then explain to them that you would like them to each make a building. Give each child their photograph and ask them to put it at the top of the notice-board. Then invite them to choose a picture of a building from those on the board. Encourage them to get the cards showing the resources that they think they will need and to collect the real items from your selection.

Remind the children that once they have their resources, they should put the cards back on to the board so that someone else can choose them.

Invite the children to make their buildings. Throughout, encourage them to work as independently as possible. Once they have completed their buildings, before they dismantle them and put them away, ask them to show their creations to the rest of the group and to talk about what they have done.

Support and extension
Speed up the resource selection for younger children by having multiple copies of each card on the board. Encourage older children to suggest what they might need before they look at the board.

Further ideas
■ Try this idea for activities other than making buildings.
■ Look at the builders on the poster showing people who help us and at the plan that they are holding. Invite each child to design a 'plan' for their building before making it.

Home links
Encourage parents and carers to have a small box of creative items that their children can select and use by themselves, such as offcuts of card, stickers and glue sticks.

Knowledge and understanding of the world

A tidy room

Learning objective
To find out about their environment and talk about those features they like and dislike.

Group size
Four or more children.

What you need
Large display board; photograph of your setting; thin paper strips; sheets of white A5 paper; drawing and writing materials.

What to do
Invite the children to talk about the pictures and whether or not they like what they see. Talk about who in the book helps to make the city a better place to live, such as the gardener and the builder.

Ask the children to look around the room. Encourage each child to tell you one thing that they like about it, and one thing that they do not like. Is it easy to find what they want? Is the room always tidy? Next, ask the children who helps to make the room look nice, for example, an adult helper, or possibly a caretaker or cleaner.

Take the children for a walk around your setting, outside the room that you are currently in. If you have an outside play area, invite them to walk around it and to talk about what they can see. Again, encourage them to talk about who helps to keep the area looking good.

Put the picture of your setting in the middle of the display board. Give each child a sheet of A5 paper and drawing and writing materials. Explain that you would like them to draw one thing about the room and draw a person who helps to make it look nice. Display the finished pictures on the board around the photograph of your setting and link them together with the thin paper strips.

Support and extension
Encourage younger children to just talk initially. Invite older children to give reasons whey they like the item that they drew.

Home links
Ask parents and carers to help their children to write down one thing that they do to help to keep the house tidy. Encourage them to bring their sentences in to share with one another.

Further idea
■ Add to the display pictures of places in the local area and the people who help to keep them looking nice.

Knowledge and understanding of the world

Who's hiding?

Learning objective
To find out about and identify some features of living things.

Group size
Four to six children.

What you need
Drawing and writing materials; sheets of white A4 card; sheets of white A5 card; scissors; sticky tape; ruler; pencil.

What to do
Make simple books by taping each sheet of A5 card on top of each sheet of white A4 card so that the short edge of the A4 card and the long edge of the A5 card are touching. Draw a line down the centre of the A4 card, where the other edge of the A5 card is touching the A4 card.

Read *In the City* and encourage the children to predict what is under each flap. Explain that you would like them to make their own lift-the-flap books. Look at the pictures of the pigeon and compare the drawing of the pigeon on the flap with the one underneath it. (Under the flap, you can see the bird's head too.) Tell the children that you would like them to each draw a picture of an animal or bird on the A4 card. Invite each child to tell you what they would like to draw and to draw it across the pencil line, so that the animal is divided and has a part on either side of the line. Encourage each child to talk about the features of the animal that they are drawing and to compare them with those of the other children's animals.

When the animal pictures are finished, invite each child to draw on their sheet of A5 card something or someone that they can use to partly hide their animal. This could be a building where we find people who help us, such as a shop, or a person from the book, such as a builder.

Support and extension
Provide support to younger children when they draw the animal features and the object or person. Invite older children to add a label explaining which part of the animal can be seen from beneath the card.

Home links
Invite the children to take their books home to show their parents or carers.

A4 card

Line down the centre

Tape

A5 card

Object or person partly hiding animal

Further idea
■ **Encourage the children to use their flap books as a starting-point for storytelling.**

Follow the firefighter

Learning objective
To move with confidence, imagination and in safety.

Group size
Four or more children.

What you need
Four or five different hats similar to those worn by people who help us, such as a firefighter's or police officer's helmet, chef's hat or builder's hard hat.

What to do
Read the book to the children and talk with them about the different people who help us and the clothes and hats that they are wearing. Show them the hats that you have collected and invite them to tell you who might wear each hat. Ask for suggestions on the actions that each of those people would do in their jobs – for example, firefighters have to climb ladders, police officers drive cars (or ride horses) and chefs need to stir the food. Take each of the helping people in turn and encourage the children to stand where they are and pretend to be that person.

Choose a child to be the 'leader'. Tell the children that you would like them to move around the room looking for spaces and avoiding one another, but watching the leader all the time. As the children move, invite the leader to choose one of the hats and to put it on. As soon as the children see the leader do this, they must stand still and pretend to do something that the wearer of the hat would do. The children continue to do this until the leader takes the hat off. Then the children can move around the room again.

Choose another leader. Ask them to select a different hat and put it on, and the rest of the children to move as before. Continue until every child has had a turn at being the leader.

Further idea
■ Have a dressing relay where the children have to race against one another to put on a uniform.

Support and extension
For younger children, begin with just two hats, preferably of very different styles and colours. For older children, use three or four hats of the same colour, such as yellow (a firefighter's hat, a builder's hard hat and a sou'wester) or white (chef, nurse and crossing patrol attendant's hats).

Home links
Give each child a hat template and ask them to take it home and decorate it. Encourage them to think about how the wearer of the hat might move.

Fill the bins

Learning objective
To use a range of small and large equipment.

Group size
Eight or more children.

What you need
At least five paper balls (screwed-up old sheets of A4 paper) or beanbags for each child; a large box for each team; large, empty floor space; coloured bands, a different colour for each team.

What to do
With the children, look in the book at the picture of the park at night. Talk about why we put rubbish in the bins, who puts it there (for example, park visitors or a park keeper) and what happens to it after it is put in the bins.

Invite the children to pretend to be park keepers and tidy up some rubbish. Divide the children up into teams of equal size. Allocate each team a colour and give everyone a band of the appropriate colour. Put a coloured band to match the team around each large box.

Scatter the paper balls or beanbags over the 'park' (large, empty floor space). Line the 'bins' (boxes) up on one side of the park, leaving some space between each of them. Check that each team knows which bin to put their balls into. Line the teams up on the other side of the park.

Explain to the children that, on a signal, you would like them to run around the area, each collecting one paper ball at a time and putting it in the bin that matches the coloured band that they are wearing.

When all the balls have been collected, count how many there are in each bin. The team with the most balls in their bin is the winner.

Support and extension
Divide younger children into just two teams, with two bins and two different-coloured bands. For older children, draw a line one metre away from each bin and invite them to throw their balls into it from behind the line.

Home links
Invite parents and carers to play a simple throwing game with their children using a wastepaper basket or cardboard box and screwed-up pieces of old paper as balls.

Further idea
■ Draw paths on to the floor of the large, empty space. Tell the children that all the areas beyond the paths are 'grass', which should not be walked on. Play the game again, this time challenging the children to pick up all the balls without touching the grass.

Hold it all

Learning objective
To express and communicate their ideas, thoughts and feelings by using a widening range of materials and suitable tools, and by designing and making.

Group size
Four to six children.

What you need
Cardboard boxes with flaps that can be used for lids; materials for decorating; play dough and tools; tools that the children might want, such as scissors or glue.

What to do
With the children, look in the book at the picture of the builder and show them the builder's bag. What do they think is in the bag? Encourage them to think about tool boxes that their parents or carers might use.

Talk with the children about the shape of the bag that the builder in the picture has. Explain that it must be large enough to contain all his tools and that it has handles to help him to carry it around. Tell the children that you would like them to each make a tool bag or box and to put some pretend tools in it. Invite them to tell you what they could use to make the bags or boxes and to explain how they want to design them.

Encourage the children to make their tool boxes, using their own designs where possible. Invite them to use a variety of materials and tools, such as scissors, rulers for straight lines and so on. Throughout, talk with the children about what they are doing.

Once the children have made their tool boxes, invite them to use the play dough to shape and form some tools that they could put inside their tool boxes. Encourage them to look in the book at the picture of the builder and the tools that he is using.

Support and extension
Invite younger children to make either the play-dough tools or the tool boxes. Encourage older children to make more detailed designs and, where possible, to draw their designs.

Home links
Ask the children to look for as many different types of boxes around their home as possible, such as those made from plastic, metal, wood or cardboard, and to compare the different types of boxes (not their shapes and sizes).

Further ideas
■ Invite the children to design overalls for a builder.
■ Encourage the children to work co-operatively, as a team of builders would do, to make a large model.

Broom, coooo, miaow

Learning objective
To observe and explore how sounds can be changed.

Group size
Four or more children.

What you need
Flip chart or easel and paper; marker pen; variety of musical instruments.

What to do
Explain to the children that the book shows not only a number of people that can help us in the city, but also a day in the life of the city. It begins with the builder arriving at work, moves on to people in a shop who are possibly on their lunch break, before finishing with a picture of a cat under a moonlit sky in the park.

Talk about the sequence of events in the story. Look at the pictures again one by one and encourage the children to find the helping people and to suggest noises that they could make – for example, the bus driver might have a horn to beep.

Invite the children to choose, as a group, three noises that could be heard on the daytime pictures and three noises that could be heard at night. With the children's help, think up a very simple picture or symbol for each of the sounds and write it on the flip chart. Encourage the children to think of ways that they can re-create each of the sounds using the different instruments and their voices.

Challenge the children to make a pattern using the different sounds, and write this on the chart. Point to each of the sounds in the pattern in turn and ask the children to make the appropriate sound for each of the pictures. Repeat as many times as you wish, changing the sequence of the sounds.

Support and extension
For younger children, begin with just one daytime noise and one night-time noise. Divide groups of older children into two, and invite half the group to play one noise while the other half plays another noise.

Home links
Invite parents and carers to help their children to write down one noise that they only hear at night, and one that they only hear during the day, which they can bring in to share with the rest of the group.

Further idea
■ **Repeat the activity above, but invite the children to play the sounds at different volumes, loud for daytime noises and quiet for night-time noises.**

Role-play

In the park

Learning objective
To respond in a variety of ways to what they see, hear, smell, touch and feel.

Group size
Four to six children.

What you need
Large, dark-green sheet (either fabric or a roll of paper); sticky tape; dark-brown corrugated card; variety of sheets of green A1 paper; colourful tissue paper; flowerpots; kitchen-roll tubes; bench; picnic hamper (filled with paper plates and pretend food); tape of sounds recorded outside.

What to do
Transform your role-play area into a park. Tape the large, green sheet to the floor to make the 'grass' and place the bench in the middle. Make tree trunks from the corrugated card and tape them to the wall. Add foliage cut from green paper to the top of the tree trunks. Make flowers by screwing up tissue paper and taping it to the top of the kitchen-roll tubes. Put the flowers in groups into the flowerpots and spread the pots around the 'park'.

With the children, look in the book at the pictures of the park and invite them to describe what they can see. Show them the park that you have created in the role-play area. Encourage them to say if it looks nice and why. Can they think of any ways that it could be improved? Does it need more flowers, or perhaps a 'lake'?

Talk about things that happen in a park, for example, people having picnics, playing ball games or reading newspapers. Encourage the children to try some of these activities, working co-operatively. Remind them that making lots of noise and playing with balls are outdoor activities.

Invite the children to think of ways to make their park more realistic. Ideas could include playing a tape of sounds recorded outside in a real park, dropping clean 'litter' for the children to put in bins, making more flowers or flowerpots, sprinkling the flowers with floral scents such as lavender, and so on.

Further idea
■ **Invite the children to sing some songs in the park for an outdoor concert.**

Support and extension
Encourage younger children to focus on how the park looks by making flowers, arranging picnic areas and so on. Invite older children to add textures to the park, for example, by making leaves for the trees from tissue paper.

Home links
Invite parents and carers to have an indoor picnic with their children.

Chapter 6

Flashing Fire Engines

This action-packed book recounts a shift for an animal fire crew. The text is written using rhymes and includes many words to describe what the firefighters can see and hear. It gives information about a fire engine and the work of firefighters, and can be used to encourage children to think about the importance of teamwork. It also contains a useful, simple glossary.

Using the book

In the Communication, language and literacy activities, the children play with lettered dice to make up rhyming words. Then some of the descriptive words from the book are used to make a collection of words connected to sight, smell and hearing. The children are also encouraged to think of words that rhyme with the names of everyday objects.

The Mathematical development activities include trying to make ladders to reach 'windows' on a box building, using a variety of shapes to make collage fire engines, and counting teddy bears on and off a fire engine.

The children pretend to be firefighters and work together to get a 'hose' to a 'fire' for one of the Personal, social and emotional activities. The other activity in this section encourages the children to role-play calling the emergency services.

In Knowledge and understanding of the world, the children look at different pieces of fabric to answer the question 'What is a good material to keep a firefighter dry?'. They also have the opportunity to program a toy to move around a large map.

The children are encouraged to travel under, over and through apparatus in the Physical development section. They also take it in turns to be the leader of firefighters travelling to different 'buildings on fire'.

In Creative development, words representing sounds are taken from the book for the children to use in sequences and patterns of noises. The children also make scenes in shoeboxes with small-world equipment for the other children to feel and describe by touch only.

The role-play area is changed into a firefighters' rest room where the children pretend to be firefighters and re-create the sequence of events from answering an emergency phone call to getting dressed and going out in the fire engine.

Communication, language and literacy

Learning objective
To hear and say initial and final sounds in words.

National Literacy Strategy
To discriminate 'onsets' from 'rimes' in speech and spelling (using knowledge of rhyme to identify families of rhyming consonant-vowel-consonant words).

Group size
Four to six children.

What you need
The photocopiable sheet on page 125; two large dice, each with a piece of white paper taped over each face; pencils.

Clever dice

What to do
On one dice, write on each face a letter that could start a three-letter word (onset), such as 'c', 't' 's' and so on. On the other dice, write two letters on each face that could end a three-letter word (rime), such as 'at', 'in', 'un' and so on. Make a copy of the photocopiable sheet for each child and write a different rime from the second dice on the bottom rung of each sheet.

Read the book to the children and explain that firefighters need to be able to climb ladders quickly to rescue people. Read the book again and encourage the children to say when they hear two words that rhyme or sound the same. Give each child a photocopiable sheet and pencil, and check that they can read the rime on their sheet. Roll both the onset and rime dice. Encourage the children to read the letters showing on the dice and to arrange them into a word. Ask each child to check their ladder to see if the rime on it matches the one on the rime dice. Help the child with the same rime to copy the onset showing on the onset dice just in front of the rime on their sheet.

Ask the children to take it in turns to roll the dice and read first the onset dice, then the rime dice to make a word. Each time a new word is rolled, encourage the child with the matching rime on their sheet to copy the word on to the next empty rung on their ladder. Carry on until a child has written a different word on every rung of their ladder, all the words rhyming since they have the same rime.

Further idea
■ **Choose one simple, short word and challenge the children to say as many words as possible that rhyme with it.**

Support and extension
For younger children, write a rime on to each rung beforehand. Encourage older children to read all the letters by themselves.

Home links
Encourage parents and carers to read rhyming books such as *Hairy Maclary* by Lynley Dodd (Puffin Books) to their children, and to sing traditional rhymes such as 'Hickory Dickory Dock'.

Communication, language and literacy

Listen, see and hear

Learning objective
To extend their vocabulary, exploring the meanings and sounds of new words.

National Literacy Strategy
To make collections of personal interest or significant words, and words linked to particular topics.

Group size
Six children.

What you need
The photocopiable sheet on page 126; three sheets of A3 card (one red, one yellow and one blue, labelled 'see', 'hear' and 'smell'); sheets of white A4 paper, each cut horizontally in four strips; writing materials.

What to do
Read the book to the children and explain that there are lots of words that tell the reader what the firefighters are seeing, hearing and smelling. Re-read the book and help the children to find as many of the words connected with the senses as possible. Check that they know the meaning of all the words.

Lay the labelled sheets of card flat on a table or on the floor and help the children to read the words. Make a copy the photocopiable sheet and cut out the words. Give each child one of the words and help them to read it. Encourage them to say if the word is connected to seeing, hearing or smelling. Invite them to put their word on to the appropriate card.

Next, encourage the children to write three sense-related words, each on a separate strip of paper: one for the sense of sight, one for the sense of hearing and one for the sense of smell. Help the children to match their words with the appropriate cards.

Support and extension
Ask younger children to write just one word, or an adult to act as a scribe for them. Invite older children to pick one of the senses and to write five words that can be used to describe it.

Home links
Suggest to parents and carers that they help their children to write down three words about smelling, seeing or tasting, which they can bring in to show the rest of the group.

Further idea
■ At the beginning of each new topic, ask the children to help you to compile a list of words that they know linked to it. Use the list for topic work during the topic and, at the end, invite the children to think of more words that they have learned over the course of the topic.

Communication, language and literacy

Rhyme time

Learning objective
To listen with enjoyment and respond to rhymes.

National Literacy Strategy
To recognize, explore and work with rhyming patterns, extending these patterns by analogy and generating new and invented words in speech and spelling.

Group size
Four or more children.

What you need
A collection of objects in a box, each with a name no longer than four letters, such as cat, dog, ring, tin and car; child-size firefighter's hat.

What to do

Explain to the children that there are lots of rhyming words in the book and give them some examples, such as 'night' and 'fight', or 'roar' and 'door'. Tell them that you would like them to think up some rhymes of their own.

Sit the children in a circle. Choose one of them to be an 'alarm' and wear the firefighter's hat. Show the children each of the items in the box. Select one of the items and ask the children, one at a time, to think of a word that rhymes with the object that you are holding. For example, if you chose a cat, rhyming words could be 'pat', 'bat', 'mat' or 'sat'. Explain to the children that they must carry on thinking of rhyming words until the child chosen to be the alarm makes a siren noise. When this happens, the children must stop what they are doing, just as real firefighters do when the siren in the fire station goes off, and the object taken from the box must be put back.

Next, encourage the child sitting next to you to choose another item from the box for the others to think of

words that rhyme with it. Choose a different child to be the alarm and wear the firefighter's hat. Continue until everyone has had a chance to select something from the box or to be the firefighter.

Support and extension

Encourage younger children to think of any rhyming word, even if it is a nonsense word or has already been said. Give older children longer words to think of rhymes for, such as 'paper' or 'table'.

Home links

Invite parents and carers to think of a short word, then to encourage their children to think of other words that rhyme with it.

Further idea
■ Invite the children to make up simple poems verbally using some of the rhyming words from the game above.

Rescue me!

Learning objective
To use developing mathematical ideas and methods to solve practical problems.

National Numeracy Strategy
To use developing mathematical ideas and methods to solve practical problems involving counting and comparing in a real or role-play context.

Group size
Four children.

What you need
Four large cardboard boxes (cover up any writing by gluing brown paper over it); marker pen; plastic or wooden bricks.

What to do
Draw large windows on the cardboard boxes and add people to make the boxes look like buildings.

Look at the picture of the firefighters rescuing the dog from the burning building. Explain to the children that when tall buildings are on fire, firefighters need to use a special platform at the top of the ladder on the fire engine to reach the endangered people and rescue them.

Show the children the cardboard-box buildings that you have made. Tell them that you would like them to pretend to be firefighters and to make ladders that reach from the bottom of the buildings to the windows where people need rescuing.

Give each child a cardboard box and invite them to select some plastic or wooden bricks. Encourage them to choose a window at the top of the box. Then ask them to stack up their plastic or wooden bricks to make a ladder that will reach from the floor to the window that they have chosen.

Once the children have experimented with this once, invite them to try again with another window on a different part of the building, but this time to predict how many bricks they think they might need, based on the number of bricks that they used for the first ladder.

Support and extension
With younger children, measure the windows as you draw them and try to make none of them any taller than ten bricks high. With older children, use taller boxes.

Home links
Encourage parents and carers to talk with their children about the height of a few objects at home and to measure their children using non-standard measures, for example, small cardboard boxes or shoeboxes.

Further idea
■ **Have a ladder-building competition with the bricks. Who can build the tallest ladder? Which stands up for longest?**

Flashing Fire Engines

Mathematical development

Fire-engine shapes

Learning objective
To use language such as 'circle' or 'bigger' to describe the size and shape of flat shapes.

National Numeracy Strategy
To use language such as 'circle' or 'bigger' to describe the shape and size of flat shapes.

Group size
Four to six children.

What you need
Pre-cut paper, card or fabric shapes in a variety of sizes and colours, ideally in the colours of a fire engine (reds, greys or silvers, blue and black); card; glue; glue spreaders.

What to do
With the children, look in the book at two or three pictures of the fire engine. Encourage them to talk about the different parts of the fire engine and what they do. Show them the glossary in the book so that they can look at close-up pictures and descriptions of some of the things found on a fire engine. As the children look at the pictures, invite them to say what shape they think each part of the fire engine is – for example, the ladder is a rectangle.

Tell the children that you would like them to make their own fire-engine pictures, using different shapes of different sizes. Show them the shapes that you have collected. Look with them at each of the types of shapes and encourage them to talk about the names of shapes and their sizes.

Invite each child to choose a piece of card to make their picture on and to glue on to it the shapes to make their fire engine. Encourage them to describe which shapes they are going to use for their picture and to compare their sizes.

Once the children have finished their pictures and the glue has dried, invite them to look at each other's pictures and to talk about the shapes that have been used.

Support and extension
Limit the shapes that you give younger children to rectangles, circles and triangles. Provide more choice of shapes and sizes for older children.

Home links
Invite parents and carers to make shape pictures with their children by looking through old magazines and cutting shapes out.

Further idea
■ Invite each child to use their shapes to make a firefighter to go on the engine.

How many firefighters?

Learning objective
To find one more or one less than a number from 1 to 10.

National Numeracy Strategy
To find one more or one less than a number from 1 to 10.

Group size
Four to six children.

What you need
Two cardboard boxes, painted to look like a fire engine and a fire station; ten small teddy bears; 20 cards, the size of playing cards, each with a number from 1 to 10; table.

What to do
Talk with the children about the events in the book and explain that firefighters work shifts, so that some of them can be resting while others are working.

Tell the children that you would like them to take it in turns to decide how many teddy bears should go on the fire engine or should rest. Put ten of the number cards in numerical order on the table, and next to them the remaining ten, face down.

Put all the bears into or next to the fire-station box. Turn over one of the number cards and invite the children to help you to read it. Explain that this is the number of firefighters who need to go on the fire engine. Encourage the children to count out the number of bears needed. Then suggest something that means that a bear needs to be added to or taken off the fire engine, such as being sick or being needed to fight a big fire. Invite the children to decide how many bears will be on the fire engine and to point to the card with the corresponding number. Put all the bears either on the fire engine or back at the station. Repeat until all the children have had the opportunity to count the bears and find the number that is one more or one less than the number of bears.

Support and extension
For younger children, use numbers to 5. Encourage older children to find number cards for the number of bears left in the fire station too.

Home links
Invite parents and carers to think of a number and to challenge their children to say which number is one more or one less than that number.

Further idea
■ **Replace the bears with the children. Invite one of the children to be the 'controller' and to count the children and decide where they should go.**

Personal, social and emotional development

Learning objective
To form good relationships with adults and peers.

Group size
Four or more children.

What you need
A firefighter's hat and uniform for each child; long piece of smooth washing line or rope; large, empty floor space; cardboard box; toy fire engine that makes a siren noise.

Further idea
■ **Remind the children that they should never try to fight a fire. Explain that they should tell a responsible adult instead.**

Fire! Fire!

What to do
Help the children to put the hats and uniforms on. Look at the pictures of the firefighters putting out the fire with water and explain to the children that the hoses are very heavy, which is why firefighters work in teams to hold them.

Hold the rope and ask a child to carry the box and the toy fire engine. Tell the children that you would like them to move around the space pretending to be firefighters. When they hear the fire engine's siren (test this so that they know what it sounds like), they must look for the cardboard box (the fire) and stand one behind the other in a line near it, while you stay at the back, holding the rope. Practise lining up with the children.

Invite the group to move around the room. Ask the child who is holding the box to put it somewhere on the floor and to start the fire engine siren. Once you have all lined up, hold one end of the rope and pass the other to the child in front of you. Encourage them to hold the rope and pass its end as quickly as possible to the child in front, and so on until the rope reaches the front of the queue. When it does, ask the child who was carrying the box to join the end of the line and invite the child at the front to put the box on the floor, while the rest of the children move around the empty space. Continue until each child has had a turn at putting the box on the floor.

Support and extension
With younger children, pass a bucket instead. Divide older children into teams and give each team a bucket. The first team to get the bucket from the back of the line to the front is the winner.

Home links
Ask parents and carers to encourage their children to work with them, for example, when making beds or washing up.

Personal, social and emotional development

It's an emergency!

Learning objective
To be confident to try new activities.

Group size
Four or more children.

What you need
The photocopiable sheet on page 111; toy telephone; small hand bell; firefighter's hat; set of headphones.

What to do
Read the book and explain to the children that when someone needs to call the fire service in an emergency, they dial '999' on the telephone and tell an operator where the firefighters are needed.

Read the words on the photocopiable sheet. Read them again and encourage the children to join in with you. Repeat, using the music to sing the words.

Sit the children in a circle, all facing towards the centre. Give one of them the toy telephone, another the hand bell, another the headphones and a fourth child the firefighter's hat. Ask the children with the headphones and the hat to put them on. Explain that the child with the hat is the 'firefighter' and the child with the headphones is the operator who will talk to the child who needs help. The child with the telephone is the person who will call for help, and the person with the bell will 'raise the alarm'.

Tell the children that you are going to sing the song together and they are going to pass the phone to each other as you do so. Explain that the child with the bell must ring it at some point in the song. Once the bell is rung, all the children must stop singing. The child with the telephone must pretend to call the telephone operator, who will ask what the emergency is and where the firefighter needs to go. The firefighter will then stand up and run to the child with the toy telephone. Then invite the children who have the objects to swap with children who have not had a turn at using any of them.

Support and extension
For younger children, omit the operator: once the bell is rung, the firefighter runs to the child who needs help, then they swap places. Invite older children to think of reasons why they might need a firefighter.

Home links
Encourage parents and carers to talk with their children about what they should do in case of a fire (fire brigades hand out free leaflets about planning fire routes).

Further idea
■ **Talk with the children about how they must only call the firefighters in an emergency.**

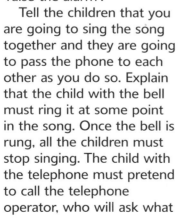

Keep me dry

Learning objective
To investigate materials by using all of their senses as appropriate.

Group size
Four children.

What you need
Shallow tray; jug of water; three or four identical-sized pieces of material of different weights and fabrics, such as silk, cotton, towelling, including one piece of a closely-woven woollen fabric; ruler; marker pen; clock.

What to do
Look at the uniforms that the firefighters wear in the pictures and the glossary at the back of the book. Talk about how the uniforms help to protect the firefighters from the heat of the flames and to keep them dry from the water of the hose.

Invite the children to hold each of the fabrics that you have selected and to talk about how they look and feel. Encourage them to predict which they think might be the best material to keep a firefighter dry.

Make a mark with a marker pen five centimetres in from the edge of a piece of material. Make an identical mark on each piece of fabric in the same place. Put a couple of centimetres of water in the shallow tray, making sure that the water is part-way up its sides, and place each piece of material into the water so that the end with the pen mark is in the water up to the mark. Let the other end of the cloth hang out of the tray. Time when the cloths were put in the water. Ask the children to guess which cloth will get the wettest first. Check each cloth after a few minutes to see if it has absorbed more water. (Compare the water level on the cloth with the pen mark.) Leave again for another few minutes. Compare the levels of water on each piece of material. Take all the cloths out and invite the children to hold them and discuss how they have changed.

Support and extension
For younger children, have just two different pieces of material. Invite older children to try one or two more pieces of cloth.

Home links
Encourage parents and carers to allow their children to wash some of their washable toys in warm water and to talk about what happens to them as they become wet.

Further idea
■ Stretch pieces of cloth over empty plastic containers (secure with an elastic band). Drip drops of water on to each material. Which drips water into the container first?

Knowledge and understanding of the world

Learning objective
To use programmable toys to support their learning.

Group size
Four children.

What you need
The photocopiable sheet on page 127; large, empty floor space; marker pen; several sheets of pale paper; sticky tape; small programmable toy or remote-controlled fire engine; scissors; small buildings, or boxes painted to look like buildings, such as a fire station and café.

Further idea
■ **Ask the children to create buildings to put on the maps.**

Take a left

What to do
Tape together the sheets of paper to obtain a very large sheet. Draw a simple map of roads, such as a square-shaped spiral, with two or three roads leading into it, wide enough to fit the programmable toy or fire engine on. Make a copy of the photocopiable sheet and cut out the boxes.

Read the book and explain that fire-engine drivers need to have good directions if they are to get quickly to where they need to go. Take the children to the map and the programmable toy or fire engine. Explain that you would like them to get the fire engine from one side of the map to the other by deciding which way to send it around the roads and passing by all the buildings.

Show the children each of the words from the photocopiable sheet and help them to read them. Check that they know which way each of the directions indicates by putting the fire engine on the floor and pushing it along in different ways, each time asking the children to find the appropriate word to describe the direction that the fire engine is travelling in.

Put the buildings in different places on the map, near the roads. Make sure that the children know what each building is. Invite them to put the fire engine next to one of the buildings, then to move it to one of the other buildings, saying the correct word when choosing the direction. Remind them to look at the arrows on the direction cards if they are unsure of which direction to select. Continue until the children have moved the toy to the other side of the map, having passed by all the buildings.

Support and extension
For younger children, begin with a simple shape, such as a square. Give older children more complicated maps to follow, for example, one with crossroads.

Home links
Invite parents and carers to use directions and directional words, such as 'Turn left here', when walking with their children.

Physical development

Keep moving!

Learning objective
To travel around, under, over and through balancing and climbing equipment.

Group size
Four or more children.

What you need
An obstacle course made up of a selection of large and small apparatus that can encourage the children to travel under, over or through (tunnels, benches, large balls, boxes, mats and so on); large, empty floor space.

What to do
Talk to the children about the types of actions that the firefighters have to do in their job, such as sliding down poles, climbing ladders or crawling into burning buildings. Show them the selection of equipment that you have laid out in the large, empty floor space.

Invite the children to try, on a given signal, each of the pieces of apparatus, making sure that they take turns and use the equipment safely. As they do this, choose some of them to show the rest of the group what they have been doing.

After the children have

showed their moves and ways of using the equipment, explain that firefighters often have to move slowly because they cannot see where they are going. They have to move with a hand outstretched so that they can feel the heat and know where the fire is. Ask the children to move slowly around the equipment, looking closely at where they put their feet.

Explain that when there is a fire, there is a lot of smoke. Tell the children that the best place to be when this happens is near the floor, crawling on hands and knees. Challenge them to do the course again, but this time on their hands and knees, and to find different ways of going around the equipment, such as under, over or through.

Support and extension
Invite younger children to go first over as many things as they safely can, then under. Challenge older children to work in pairs, one of the children trying the course with their eyes closed while the other gives them instructions.

Home links
Ask parents and carers to talk with their children about their actions around the house and when out and about, such as going upstairs or through a gate.

Further idea
■ **Invite the children to help you to arrange the apparatus.**

To the rescue

Learning objective
To move with control and co-ordination.

Group size
Four or more children.

What you need
Six sheets of A3 paper, each with a different building drawn on, such as a school, place of worship, supermarket and so on; firefighter's hat.

What to do
With the children, look in the book at the pictures of the animals in the buildings. Then show them the pictures of buildings that you have drawn and check that they know what each building is. On the floor of the large, empty space, spread out, face up, the sheets of paper.

Choose one of the children to be a leader and to wear the firefighter's hat. Invite the other children to line up behind that child. On a given signal, encourage the 'firefighter' to tell the others how he would like them to move, to which building they need to go to and then to follow him. Repeat this until each child has had a turn at being the firefighter.

As a variation, invite the firefighter to sometimes call out on the way to one building that there is a fire in another building and that they need to run

there first. The children could also perform different actions at each of the buildings when they get there.

Support and extension
Invite younger children to just follow in a line from one building to another, without moving in different ways. Divide older children into groups and give each group a different-coloured band for each of the team members to wear. Invite one child to be the leader and to tell each of the groups to go to a different building so that the children have to listen to a colour as well as to how to move and where to go.

Home links
Encourage parents and carers to invite their children to move around the house safely, in different ways – for example, they could jump or hop on one leg.

Further idea
■ Divide the children into groups, each group performing separate actions at an imaginary fire station, for example, cleaning a fire engine. Explain that when you ring a bell, you would like the children to form a line behind the leader and follow their instructions. Once the children have all got to the building and put the fire out, ask them to get back into their groups.

Creative development

Favourite noises

Learning objective
To recognize repeated sounds and patterns in music.

Group size
Four or more children.

What you need
A selection of instruments.

What to do

Read the book to the children, including the words on the illustrations. Then encourage the children to tell you which sounds they liked and remembered hearing when you read the book. Tell the children that you are going to re-read the book and that you would like them to listen carefully to the words and to tell you when they hear any word that sounds like a noise, such as 'plop' or 'dring'. When you have finished reading, invite the children to tell you which noise they like the most.

Pick four of the five different noises found on the illustrations. Divide the children into four groups and give each group a different noise. Check that each group knows the sound that you gave them by calling out the appropriate word and waiting for a response.

Explain to the children that you want them to make a pattern using the noises that they were given. Invite them to help you to decide on a sequence for the noises. Encourage each child to repeat their group's noise at the appropriate time in the pattern. To help the children to remember the order of sounds, sit the groups in the correct order in a line or a circle. On a given signal, invite the children to begin. Once they have experimented with this two or three times, encourage them to try changing the sequence of the sounds or repeating the sounds – for example, two 'whoosh', one 'weeooo' and two 'dring'.

Support and extension

Initially, divide younger children into two groups, moving on to three groups when they are more competent. Invite older children to try making their noises in different ways, such as slowly, fast, quietly or high.

Home links

Invite parents and carers to sing with their children songs that make noises, for example, 'The Wheels on the Bus' (Traditional).

Further ideas
■ Challenge the children to repeat the activity above, this time overlapping the sounds, for example, two groups making the same noise at the same time.
■ Invite one of the groups to constantly repeat their sound, while the other groups take it in turns to make their noises.

Feel your way

Learning objective
To explore texture, shape, form and space in two or three dimensions.

Group size
Four children.

What you need
Four large shoeboxes, each with a large hole cut in its side; the shoeboxes' lids; variety of small-world equipment, such as doll's house furniture and small plastic figures; old offcuts of fabric and carpet.

What to do
Talk with the children about the people that the firefighters in the book help. Explain that often in a fire there is a lot of smoke and this makes it hard for a firefighter to see where they are going, so they need to use their sense of touch. Tell the children that you would like each of them to make a simple room in a box for the other children to feel. Then explain that you would like them to make the rooms without telling the other children what they look like.

Show the children the shoeboxes and the small-world equipment that you have collected. Hand out a shoebox to each child and invite them to choose some objects to put in it. Ask them not to put too many things in their box and encourage them to choose objects that have a variety of textures and shapes that can be felt easily. Remind them that the colours of the items are not important because the 'rooms' are to be felt and not seen.

When the children have finished their rooms, invite them to put the lids on the boxes. Then ask them to take it in turns to close their eyes, put one hand into the hole in each box and try to describe what they can feel. Once all the children have felt all the boxes, invite each child to remove their box's lid so that the other children can compare what they felt with what was really there.

Support and extension
Help younger children to choose just four or five different objects for their boxes. Encourage older children to talk about the textures of the resources that they select.

Home links
Ask parents and carers to invite their children to hold things and describe them using as many of their senses as possible, including sight.

Further idea
■ Encourage the children to make collage pictures that use a variety of different textures.

Role-play

Ready to go!

Learning objective
To use talk to organize, sequence and clarify thinking, ideas, feelings and events.

Group size
Four to six children.

What you need
Four chairs; two tables; plates and cutlery; pretend food; four mats on the floor; small bell; four firefighters' uniforms including helmets; large cardboard box painted to look like a fire engine, in which four children can sit; pen; paper; small box painted to look like a television; toy telephone.

What to do
Arrange one of the tables and the chairs on the far side of the role-play area, with the table set and the television near it. On the other side of the role-play area, put the uniforms and the fire engine. Place the toy telephone, bell, pen and paper on the second table, in the centre of the area.

Read the book and look at the last spread, which shows the firefighters resting before being called out to deal with a fire again. Discuss with the children the types of things that the firefighters do in a rest room. Show them the pictures of the firefighters getting dressed inside the fire station and talk about what they must do to get ready.

Take the children to the role-play area and explain that it is a firefighters' rest room. Show them the fire engine and the uniforms. Next, encourage them to pretend to be firefighters. Remind them that they will have to work as a team, just as the firefighters in the book do.

Invite the children to re-create the sequence of events that real firefighters follow, such as answering the telephone, raising the alarm (ringing the bell), getting dressed and going off in the fire engine. Encourage the children to make up events for the firefighters to deal with, based on their knowledge of firefighters and fire engines, such as someone needing a cat rescued from a tree, a fire in a building or someone who has fallen down a deep hole.

Support and extension
Provide more fire engines for younger children and encourage them to work in pairs. Invite older children to make their stories longer.

Further ideas
■ Invite the children to make fire-prevention safety posters for the walls of the role-play area.
■ Help the children to make a 'rota' for when they can play in the role-play area.

Home links
Ask parents and carers to talk with their children about the importance of the different emergency services and what they do for the community.

A day at work

I enjoy my job. I work in a big department store in the city. Each day I travel to work on a bus. It takes a long time. The bus is always busy in the morning and filled with people who work in the city or want to go shopping. The bus passes a big building site. They are building a new swimming-pool. There are always lots of bulldozers and diggers on the site.

The bus station is just across the road from the shop where I work, so I don't have to walk too far. The city is busy and there are lots of people, cars, shops and pigeons. There are pigeons everywhere. During the day, they walk around on the pavements and sit on the rooftops or the window-ledges.

The shop I work in is one of the biggest in the city. You can buy almost anything there, from clothes and toys to pots and pans and books. The toy department is on the ground floor, next to the clothing department. I take money from people when they want to buy the toys and put it in the till. I like seeing all the happy children's faces when they go out of the shop with their new toys. When the shop is quiet, I help to put the new toys out on the shelves so boys and girls can look at them.

I like to take my packed lunch to the park at dinner time, if the weather is nice. There are some lovely flowers and plants there. The gardeners are very busy and are always working. When I'm in the park, I sometimes see people walking their dogs.

After my dinner, I go back to the shop and help people again until it is time to go home. At half past five, I leave the shop, walk back to the bus station, and catch a bus to take me home again.

Sometimes, though, I go back to the park. I've heard music concerts in the park, and there is usually a big fireworks display there each November.

But the city doesn't stop when the shops shut. Late at night people still need to walk their dogs, and the builders and gardeners sometimes work through the night. And people even look in the shop windows to see what they can buy when the shop opens again in the morning.

Lorraine Gale

Getting better

Your pink pill

Doctor, doctor,
Please come quick!
My doll is feeling
Very sick.

Doctor, doctor,
Your pink pill
Has stopped my dolly
Feeling ill.

Brenda
Williams

Poor little Jenny

Poor little Jenny
Has a pain in her head.
Poor little Jenny
Must stay in bed.

Sleep little Jenny
Till the pain goes away.
Wake little Jenny
You can run and play.

Brenda Williams

I've got a cold!

Sniffle, snuffle, sniff and sneeze
Cough and splutter, puff and wheeze.

My throat is sore, my nose is runny
And my tummy's feeling funny.

Have some medicine, go to bed
That is what the doctor said.

Tucked up warm, but feeling low,
I'm better in a day or so!

Brenda Williams

Guess who?

I wear a yellow hat.
I help to put out fires.
I drive a fire engine.
Who am I?

I wear a white coat.
You see me when you are ill.
I help to make you well.
Who am I?

I have a big, blue and red bag.
There are lots of letters in it.
I bring them to your house.
Who am I?

I ask you what you want to eat.
I write your order down.
I bring you your food.
Who am I?

Lorraine Gale

Photocopiable

We are friends all dancing

Johanne Levy

Be my friend

Johanne Levy

Who wears a hard hat?

2. Who gives us medicine?
The doctor gives us medicine. *(and so on)*

3. Who reads us stories?
The teacher reads us stories. *(and so on)*

4. Who grows our crops?
The farmer grows our crops. *(and so on)*

5. Who wears a helmet?
The policeman wears a helmet. *(and so on)*

Johanne Levy

The firefighter

The phone we must use, There's no time to lose, Our house__ is burn - ing down! That's

why just in time, We ring 9 9 9, And then the fire - fight - er comes round.

Johanne Levy

To my best friend

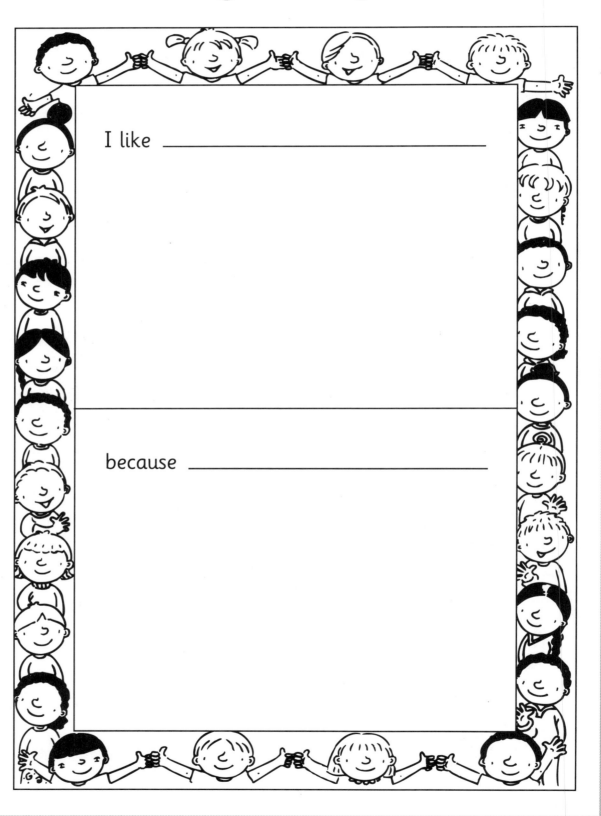

I like _____

because _____

Friendly or unfriendly?

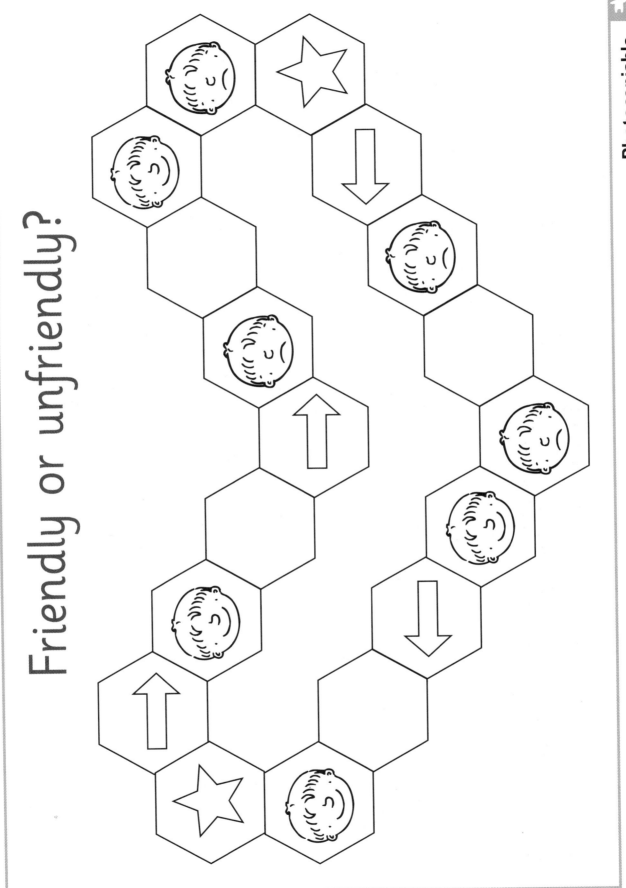

A trip to the doctor's

We went home in the car.
Freddie felt better.
The chemist got Freddie's medicine.
The doctor looked into our mouths.
Mum took Freddie and me to the doctor's in the car.
Freddie had some pink medicine on a spoon.

Make me feel better!

Patient's name: _____

Diagnosis and treatment: _____

_____

Signed: _____

Health game

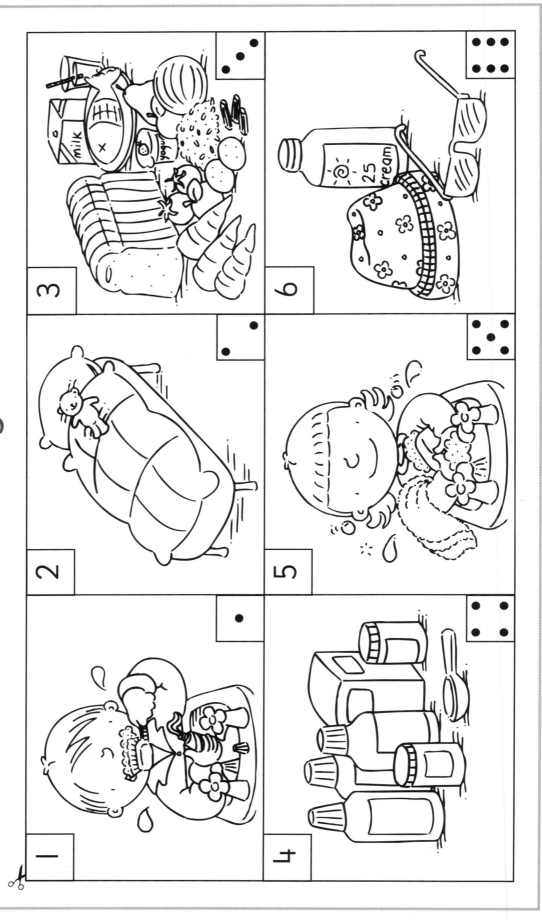

Passengers on a bus

How many bags?

Photocopiable

My waistcoat

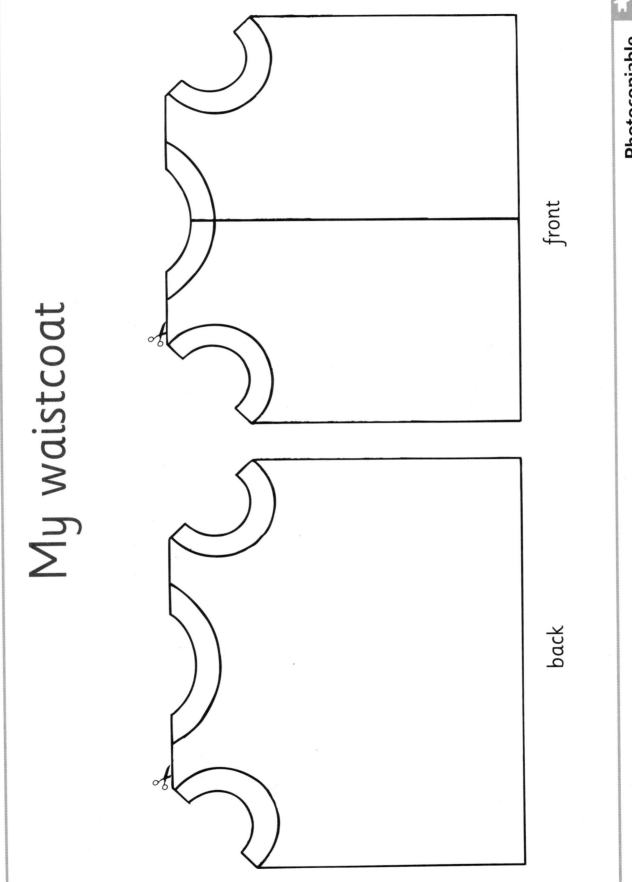

front

back

Young and old

People who help us

Theme Centre
for early years

Guess the letter

l		e	
	k		s
o		v	
	t		g
h		c	

My teeth

What do I need?

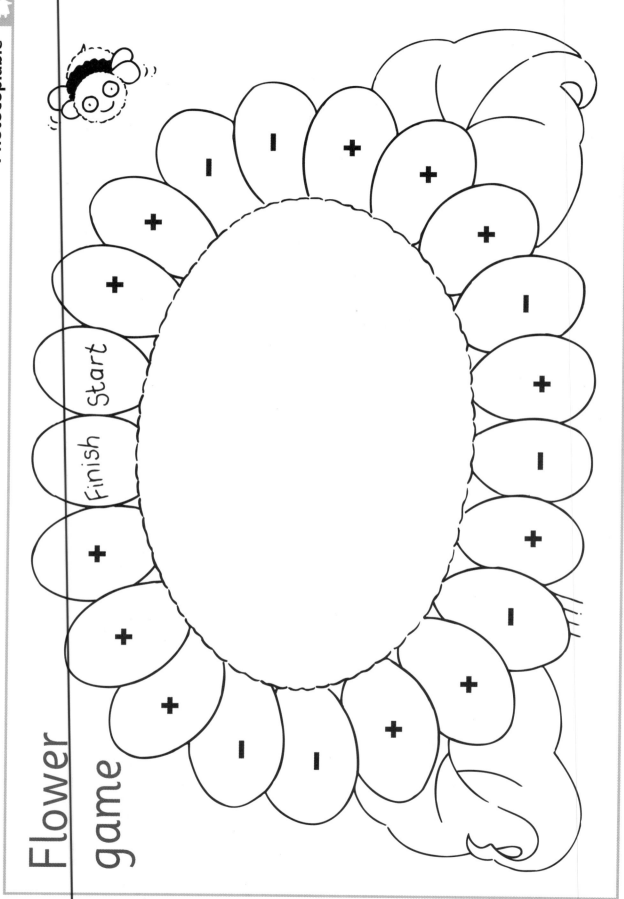

Start

Finish

Flower game

Rhyming ladders

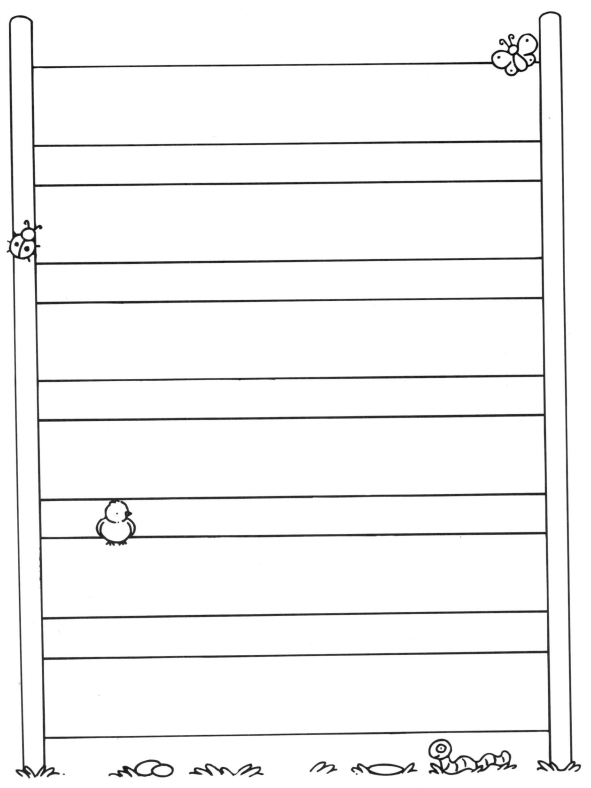

Words for the senses

blaze	smoke
roar	flash
plop	sizzle

Photocopiable

Choose the direction

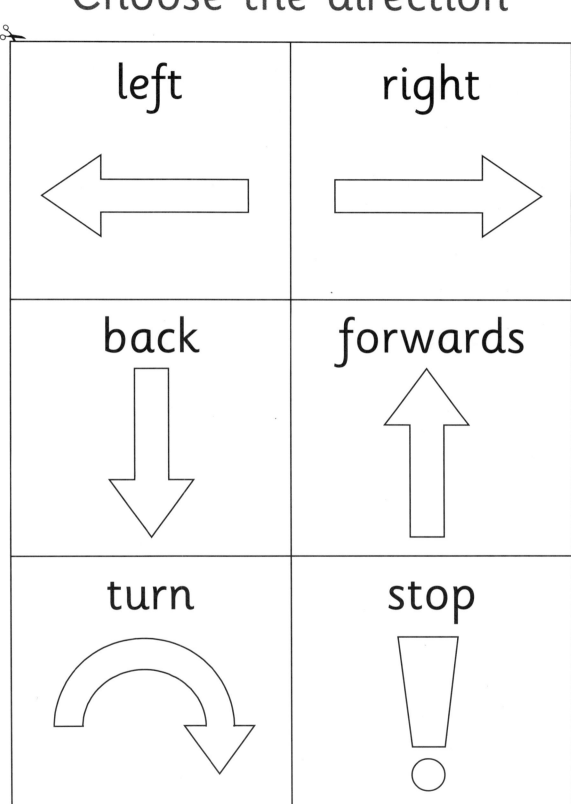

left	right
back	forwards
turn	stop

Useful resources

Children's books
■ *Jobs People Do* (Dorling Kindersley, Board Book, ISBN 0-75135-518-6)
■ *Firefighters* by Rod Campbell (Campbell Books, Board Book, ISBN 1-8529-2211-7)
■ *A Day in the Life of a Doctor* by Carol Watson (Franklin Watts, PB, ISBN 0-7496-3615-7)
■ *A Day in the Life of a Firefighter* by Carol Watson (Franklin Watts, PB, ISBN 0-7496-3618-1)
■ *A Day in the Life of a Postman* by Carol Watson (Franklin Watts, PB, ISBN 0-7496-3616-5)
■ *A Day in the Life of a Vet* by Carol Watson (Franklin Watts, PB, ISBN 0-7496-3619-X)
■ *A Day In The Life Of A Police Officer* by Carol Watson (Franklin Watts, PB, ISBN 0-7496-4100-2)
■ *Say Aah! My First Visit to the Doctor* by Jen Green and Mike Gordon (Hodder Wayland, PB, ISBN 0-75022-820-2)
■ *When I Grow up I Want to Be...* by Blaise Douglas and Tania Hurt-Newton (Walker Books, PB, ISBN 0-7445-5233-8)
■ *What Am I?* by Debbie MacKinnon (Frances Lincoln, Board Book, ISBN 0-7112-0954-5)

Teachers' books
■ *People Who Help Us* by Anne Farr and Janet Morris (*Themes for Early Years* series, Scholastic, PB, ISBN 0-590-53463-7)
■ *People Who Help Us* by Susan Gray (*Early Years Wishing Well* series, Scholastic, PB, ISBN 0-439-01979-6)
■ *Our World Displays* (*Themes on Display for Early Years* series, Scholastic, PB, ISBN 0-439-01738-6)

Games and puzzles
■ *People Who Help Us Puzzle* (Set 1 – Doctor and Nurse, Fireman at Work, Police Lady and Life Boat, code: LV633/097) is a set of four sturdy 42-piece jigsaws. From Hope Education, Hyde Buildings, Ashton Road, Hyde, Cheshire SK14 4SH. Tel: 08451-202055.
■ *People Who Help Us Puzzle* (Set 2 – Dinner Lady, Bus Driver, Dentist and Lollipop Lady, code: LW633/097) is a set of four sturdy 42-piece jigsaws. From Hope Education, address above.
■ *Who Can Help? Lotto Game* (code: LR003/099) is a game where the player matches helpers with the situations in which they can help. From Hope Education, address above.

Equipment
■ *Dressing Up Clothes* include clothes for a Doctor, Post Person, Male Nurse, Police Person, Nurse, Lollipop Person, Fire Person and Chef (code: different for each outfit). From Hope Education, address above.
■ *Occupational Puppets* (code: ZZ903/095) are a set of eight screen-printed hand puppets, each depicting a different profession. The reverse of each puppet shows the rear of the uniform. The set includes a firefighter, female nurse, police officer and post person. From Hope Education, address above.
■ *Multicultural Career Puppets* (code: LW010/099) are a set of ten multicultural career puppets, including Nurse (female), Construction Worker, Policewoman, Postman, Firefighter, Doctor and Chef. From Hope Education, address above.

Software
■ *Switch on Travel* (PC/MAC). From Granada Learning Ltd, Quay Street, Manchester M60 9EA. Tel: 0161-8272927.
■ *At the Doctor's* (Windows CD-ROM). From Semerc, Granada Learning Ltd, address above.

Websites
■ http://www.fireservice.co.uk (fire brigade site with online jigsaws, colouring page, book lists and teachers' notes)
■ http://www.welephant.co.uk (includes links to local fire brigades)

A Century of R

around Birmingham
and the West Midlands
VOLUME ONE
1900 – 1947

A member of the 3900 Class hauls a local train up the 1:47 gradient at the north end of Birmingham Snow Hill, c.1914. The rake of non-corridor five-compartment carriages is dwarfed by the locomotive. It was a member of the Great Western's first class of tank engine to have the 2-6-2 wheel arrangement, designed by George Jackson Churchward in 1903. There were eighty members of the class, all fitted with superheaters in 1909. They were ideally suited for their intended purpose, heavy local passenger trains. The new power box, with almost no visible means of support, still controlled semaphore signalling. Today, the tracks have been replaced by those of the Jewellery Line and the Midland Metro, but some of the buildings which form the backdrop remain unchanged.

(Roger Carpenter collection)

a personal selection by
JOHN BOYNTON

INTRODUCTION

Railmen pose proudly with LNWR Webb Tank No. 2353, around 1900. The location is unknown, but is believed to be Wolverhampton.
(Alex Chatwin collection)

So much has happened to the railways around Birmingham and the West Midlands during the twentieth century that any book attempting to include everything of interest would be heavy, expensive and probably unreadable. I have opted to be selective and, in order to include as much material as possible, to produce two volumes. This first part ends where the LMS and GWR became part of the newly nationalised British Railways network on 1st January 1948.

There are five chapters, each containing a diary of events and notes for one decade, followed by at least one article. The first chapter, for example, features the development of better links between the West Midlands and London following the introduction of two-hour expresses between Birmingham New Street and Euston in 1905. Probably the most visible improvement to the ordinary traveller in the second decade of the century was the transformation of Birmingham Snow Hill into one of the finest stations in the country, and this is described in Chapter Two.

Subsequent chapters follow a similar pattern, although it has been undesirable, not to say impossible, to contain features within a rigid area or time zone. An account of the route over the Lickey Incline appears in Chapter Three, because 'Big Bertha' began work as the Lickey banker in 1920, but this has not prevented me from using photographs or describing events which happened before 1920 and after 1929.

Locomotives and their development merit special mention, hardly surprising when considering the huge range of machines that was once so familiar throughout the area. The newest express locomotives at the beginning of the century, built in 1900, were the beautiful single-wheelers, the 'spinners' of the Midland Railway. In little under half a century top-link locomotive design had passed through "Kings" and "Patriots" to arrive at main line diesel No.10000, completed by the LMS in December 1947. Stanier Pacific No.6256 "Sir William A.Stanier

F.R.S." entered service in the same month; one of its nameplates now hangs in the lobby of Stanier House, Birmingham, on the site of the Midland Railway's Central Goods Depot. Many nineteenth century locomotives were still hard at work into the 1930s and beyond - it would be wrong to ignore them. On the other hand, some of the best photographs of locos built before 1947 were taken during the 1950s and 60s, so they are also included.

Any book claiming to describe the railways of the Birmingham area would be incomplete if it failed to mention something of the huge amount of train building that went on, an activity which continues to this day. Construction of the Eurostar trains at GEC Alsthom Metro-Cammell's works at Washwood Heath is merely a recent chapter in a success story that goes back almost to the beginning of railways. The period before 1947, particularly the way in which the company fought off the recession of the 1930s by securing orders as railways began to modernise, is an important part of the whole picture.

This first volume concludes with the Second World War and its aftermath, as the railways slowly began to recover. Memories of those who were there can be both interesting and humorous. I have included the thoughts of men who worked on the railway, and some who travelled on it in the less than ideal conditions of the 1940s. On Saturdays or during school holidays, large numbers of boys often gathered at important stations or near a main lines to soak in the atmosphere. They have not been forgotten. A few boys took pictures with a Brownie box camera; other people were already using colour film in the 1930s and 40s. This work, and the scenes they recorded, are now part of railway history and as such they are included in these pages.

John Boynton
1997

Birmingham New Street, London & North Western platforms, 1905. The photographer had access to the screen at the west end of the roof, from where he took this picture. From left to right are the Queen's Hotel, the Stour Valley bays, platforms 1, 2 and 3. Both faces of the narrow island platform were known as Platform 2 – potentially very confusing. Signalling was not necessarily much clearer. Of the three signal arms on Platform 1, the one on the left controlled movement along the full length of the platform; the middle arm, with ring, was for movement over the crossover; the right-hand arm, also with ring, protected the through road. These signals were controlled from No.3 Cabin, perched on the footbridge and over the through roads. The ramps led down to the Post Office subway, from which members of the public were barred. It connected all the main platforms with each other and with the city's head post office in nearby Hill Street. A similar subway near the other end of the platforms was for public use, an alternative to the footbridge.   *(National Railway Museum)*

CONTENTS

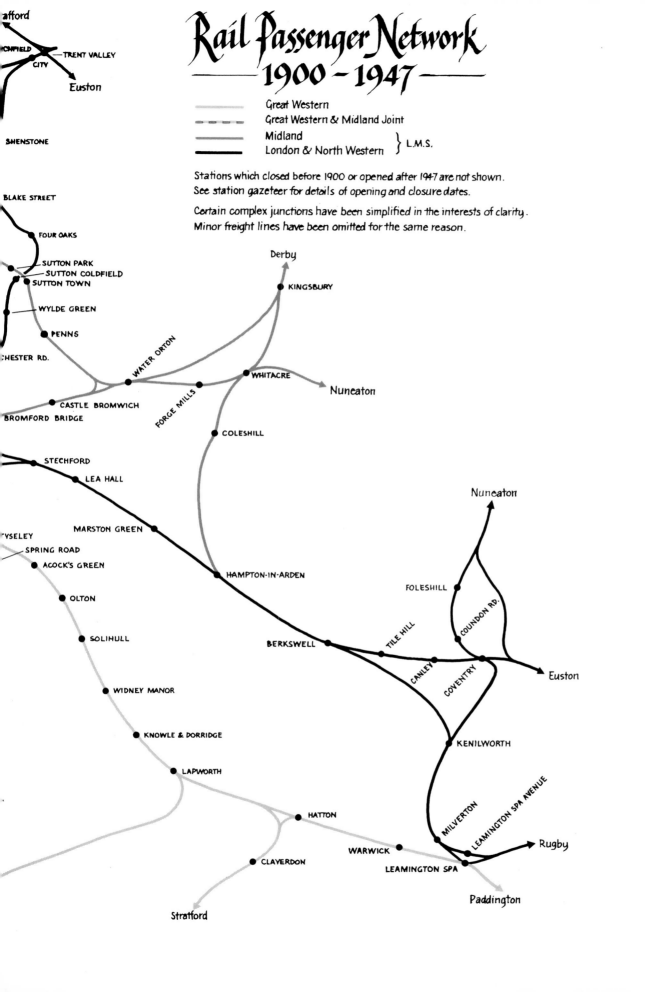

Rail Passenger Network
— 1900 – 1947 —

——————	Great Western
– – – – – –	Great Western & Midland Joint
——————	Midland
——————	London & North Western } L.M.S.

Stations which closed before 1900 or opened after 1947 are not shown.
See station gazeteer for details of opening and closure dates.

Certain complex junctions have been simplified in the interests of clarity.
Minor freight lines have been omitted for the same reason.

afford

CHFIELD — TRENT VALLEY
CITY

Euston

SHENSTONE

BLAKE STREET

FOUR OAKS

SUTTON PARK
SUTTON COLDFIELD
SUTTON TOWN

WYLDE GREEN

PENNS

CHESTER RD.

Derby

KINGSBURY

WATER ORTON

WHITACRE

Nuneaton

CASTLE BROMWICH
BROMFORD BRIDGE

FORGE MILLS

COLESHILL

STECHFORD

LEA HALL

YSELEY

SPRING ROAD

MARSTON GREEN

ACOCK'S GREEN

OLTON

HAMPTON-IN-ARDEN

Nuneaton

SOLIHULL

FOLESHILL

COUNDON RD.

TILE HILL

BERKSWELL

WIDNEY MANOR

CANLEY

COVENTRY

Euston

KNOWLE & DORRIDGE

KENILWORTH

LAPWORTH

LEAMINGTON SPA AVENUE

HATTON

MILVERTON

CLAVERDON

WARWICK

Rugby

LEAMINGTON SPA

Paddington

Stratford

CHAPTER ONE : 1900-1909

[Diary : Notes : Two Hours To London : Cross Country and Suburban through Warwickshire]

Diary

1900

Single-wheeler 'Spinner' locos built by the Midland Railway.

July 30th – The independent Birmingham North Warwickshire & Stratford-upon-Avon Railway, which had obtained powers to build a line between Birmingham and Stratford in 1894, absorbed by GWR.

1901

August 17th – Act authorising construction of a Wolverhampton & Cannock Chase Railway, linking the Great Western and LNWR at Wolverhampton with the LNWR at Cannock, a distance of six miles. This would have been a useful extra freight link for the South Staffs coalfield but powers to build the line lapsed, although it was still being seriously discussed as late as 1926.

September – The main LNWR goods yard for Birmingham, at Windsor Street, Aston, was extended, giving it a capacity of 800 wagons. The yard also served Birmingham Corporation's main gasworks.

October 1st – New station opened at Stourbridge Junction, GWR. The old station, a quarter of a mile to the north, was closed, and the junction with the Stourbridge Town branch realigned, to face south rather than north. The 1901 buildings remain largely intact and the station was refurbished in 1996.

1902

First "Saint" Class locos built by GWR.

First Johnson 4-4-0 three cylinder compound locos built by Midland Railway.

January 1st – New LNWR station opened at Newton Road, on the Birmingham-Walsall line. The third station of this name, it was close to the site of the original Grand Junction station of 1837. The second station (1863-1902), was briefly named West Bromwich, more in hope than in geographical accuracy.

March 10th – Deepfields station (now Coseley) opened by the LNWR on the Stour Valley Line, replacing the original 1852 station, which was a quarter of a mile to the north.

June 2nd – First non-stop trains between Euston and New Street, taking two hours five minutes.

1903

First 2800 Class locos built by GWR.

January 1st – Hazelwell station opened on the Camp Hill line.

1904

First "Precursor" Class locos built by LNWR.

1905

First 4500 Class tank locos built by GWR.

February 13th – First GWR bus service in the Midlands, linking Stourbridge Town with Belbroughton. The service was later extended to Bromsgrove.

March 1st – First two-hour expresses between Birmingham New Street and Euston.

July 1st – Coombes Holloway Halt opened, Halesowen line.

September – Old Hill High Street, Darby End and Baptist End opened, all halts on the 'Bumble Hole' loop line between Old Hill and Dudley.

1906

First "Star" locos built by GWR.

October 1st – Tyseley station opened.

1907

December 9th – North Warwickshire Line opened to goods traffic.

1908

March 2nd – Landywood Halt opened on the Walsall-Rugeley line.

July 1st – North Warwickshire Line opened to passengers. The new station at Henley replaced the town's small terminus on the branch from Lapworth, opened in 1894. The branch remained open and was provided with a connection onto the new line. The branch left the GW main line at Rowington Junction and trains ran from Lapworth. The branch station continued in use for goods traffic until 1962; branch passenger trains continued through the old station and ran, via a connecting line on a rising gradient of 1:55, into a side platform at the new station, which has never had goods facilities.

July 10th – New junction at Leamington East improved the track layout, making possible the easy introduction of new cross-country services.

1909

March 1st – Rushall station closed, due to competition from trams on the Walsall Wood route.

May 3rd – Kingsbury-Water Orton cut-off line opened.

July 1st – Birmingham Moor Street opened to passengers and to North Warwickshire Line local trains, which had temporarily terminated at Tyseley for exactly a year. The station was still unfinished.

Notes

The early years of the twentieth century were a time of renewal and development for all the railway companies that served Birmingham and the West Midlands. A whole range of successful locomotives was built, new stations were added to the system and existing ones were improved. The North Warwickshire Line opened to local and long distance traffic. Increasing competition stimulated an ever improving service on both routes to London, and rising passenger demand led to a wider variety of cross country services.

On the Midland Railway, some locos built in 1900 used a 4-2-2 wheel arrangement, considered obsolete more than twenty years earlier. These were the 'Spinners', a last beautiful throwback to an earlier age. They had huge driving wheels, 6'9" diameter, and were designed by Samuel Johnson in 1899. Earlier single wheelers slipped easily on wet rails or with a heavy train but these locos were fitted with a high-powered sander which used compressed air from their Westinghouse braking system. This one modification made them much more reliable and free-running than their predecessors. They were also economical with coal and easy to drive. It is generally agreed that these were amongst the most elegant and well-proportioned locomotives ever built. The photograph of a spinner piloting a train up the Lickey Incline (page 45) bears this out.

Johnson also designed 4-4-0 express passenger locos, both simple and compound. The compounds, with high and low pressure cylinders, were developed by his successor, Richard Deeley, after 1904. Despite the success and fame of these locos the Midland was not really moving with the times. For over thirty years they had had a 'small engine' policy, and the double heading of most important expresses was routine. As trains lengthened, the real but unfulfilled need was for larger and more powerful locos. Compounds double-headed their trains, while the spinners were reduced to piloting or handling lighter trains. There were still three spinners shedded at Bournville in 1916, well suited to the semi-fast trains of little over 100 tons which ran between New Street and Peterborough.

Midland carriages were amongst the best and most

Midland Railway loco No.758, built at Derby to a 1901 design of Samuel Johnson. These 4-4-0s passenger engines had 6' 9" driving wheels, were originally provided with bogie tenders and had four digit numbers, 26xx. They were re-numbered as the 700 Class in 1907. William Fowler later rebuilt them, adding the benefits of superheating as he did so. Photographed about 1908, the loco is on the New Street turntable, on the site now occupied by the 1966 power box. *(Roger Carpenter collection)*

comfortable in the country, thanks in particular to two Carriage & Wagon Superintendents, James Clayton and his successor David Bain, who took charge in 1902. Between them these two gentlemen established the excellent reputation of Derby's carriage works at Litchurch Lane.

The London & North Western also had a small engine policy but when George Whale succeeded Francis Webb in 1903, that soon changed. The "Precursor" 4-4-0 of 1904 strengthened all main line trains, enabling the Euston-Birmingham expresses to be accelerated and hauled by a single loco. The tank version of this class first appeared in 1906. They were used for heavier suburban trains. Both types of Precursor can be seen on shed at Monument Lane (page 62).

George Jackson Churchward was appointed Chief Mechanical Engineer of the GWR in 1902. He immediately began work on a new express passenger type, the 4-6-0 "Saints", followed by the "Stars" of 1906. The Saints established a distinctive new shape for Great Western locos which, with few variations in outward appearance, lasted until the end of steam. The profiles of the chimney, boiler, safety vale, cab and tender were Churchward hallmarks which his two successors were content to incorporate into their own designs.

Less glamorous, but just as vital, was the need for a new and more powerful heavy goods engine, fulfilled by the 160 plus members of the 2800 Class 2-8-0s, introduced in 1903. The locos had the power to pull heavy freight trains reliably, with their high boiler pressure (225lb/sq.in.) and the grip on the track exerted by eight small driving wheels (4' 7½").

Churchward's 4500 Class of 2-6-2 tank engines (1905) showed what could happen when larger locos were built in unimproved premises. (When new these were briefly 3101 Class locos, number series 21xx and 31xx.) Ten were built at Wolverhampton Stafford Road but they were too long to leave the works by the normal route, even with their buffers removed. A temporary exit track was laid through the wheel shop, on sharp curves, and across the inspection pits! The pony trucks were removed and the locos – now bufferless 0-6-0s – were eased along the track by a gang of men wielding pinch bars and out through the wheel shop via a hole knocked through the wall. All very entertaining, unless you were in charge of a pinch bar, but hardly efficient or high tech. It was this fiasco which brought locomotive building at Wolverhampton to an end, after 2180 (later 4519) emerged through the hole in the wall in April 1908.

Renewal was not confined to locomotives. The opening of the North Warwickshire Line, the 2 hour expresses to London and the development of cross country services are all featured later in this chapter. The rebuilding of Snow Hill and associated works (Chapter Two) was complete by 1912, but the work began in 1906.

Windsor Street goods yard, Aston, was extended in 1901 and in 1907 an Act was passed for an important freight route, the Coventry Loop Line, to serve the growing needs of industry.

Suburban stations were rebuilt to cope with increased use, from the Midland's Water Orton to the Great Western's Stourbridge Junction and the LNWR's Rotton Park Road. New halts were built, including three on the Old Hill-Dudley 'Bumble

Hole' Line in 1905, although looking at photographs of them in later years it is hard to imagine a time when they were not in a state of decay.

There were a few clouds on the horizon. The railways were having to experiment with 'railmotors' as a way of keeping the costs of more lightly used services within reasonable bounds. These single carriage trains, with a mini-locomotive built in to one end, could be driven from either end. They began operating on some services linking Walsall with Lichfield and Rugeley at the beginning of 1906. They had seats for 48 passengers and were divided into two 3rd class compartments, smoking and non-smoking. Their GWR counterparts worked some North Warwickshire Line local trains from its opening. The car and lorry posed no threat as yet, but for many local journeys a regular, cheap and frequent electric tram service was much better than the train. Suburban stations near a tram route generally had a bleak future. Closures for this reason had begun before 1900. Bentley, on the Midland's Walsall-Wolverhampton Line, had been used by only 206 passengers during 1892! Incredibly, it stayed open until the end of September 1898. Rushall, far too close for comfort to the Walsall-Walsall Wood tram line, closed in 1909. More would follow . . .

Two Hours To London

The London & Birmingham Railway opened between Euston and Birmingham Curzon Street in April 1838, with a service of six passenger trains each way. The three first class trains completed the 112$\frac{1}{2}$ mile journey in 5 hours 37 minutes, but the mixed trains took 6 hours 14 minutes. On 1st June 1854 Curzon Street was abandoned to goods and occasional excursion traffic when New Street was fully opened. The London & North Western's line between New Street and Wolverhampton, the Stour Valley Line, had opened to local traffic in 1852, but now the London expresses were able to use it as a through route.

The Great Western route between Paddington and Snow Hill opened as a mixed gauge line in October 1852. The broad gauge expresses took 2¾ hours for the 129¼ mile route via Oxford, while the best LNW trains covered the 113¼ miles via Rugby in 3 hours. Within two months the Great Western trains had also been slowed to 3 hours. Broad gauge was replaced by standard gauge between Snow Hill and Wolverhampton in 1868 and between Snow Hill and Paddington in the following year. Brunel's relatively primitive express locomotives had been routinely capable of sustained running at 60mph in the 1840s, so had the potential of broad gauge technology ever been developed, it is certain that two-hour expresses would have been running to Birmingham well before 1900. Apart from that, there were two obstacles to improvements on the Birmingham line. George Nugent Tyrrell was Superintendent of all Great Western lines between 1864 and 1888, ruling with an unfortunate mix of caution and complacency. For someone in his position, his fear of speed was bizarre. As locomotive designs and train speeds were steadily improving elsewhere he imposed a ban preventing any trains – even the best expresses – from exceeding 40mph. In addition to Tyrrell's dead hand, the route itself was far from direct, one of several large kinks in the company's main lines which caused it to be known as the Great Way Round.

A more direct route did not open until 1910. Meanwhile, crucial changes in top management during the 1890s eventually lead to lasting improvements. Earl Cawdor was appointed as the energetic young Chairman in 1895 and, unlike many others in a similar position, took a keen 'hands on' interest in the railway, preferring to earn his salary rather than merely draw it. The new General Manager, James Wilkinson, was quoted in the "GWR Magazine" (April 1899) as saying that:–

"We are trying to make ours the biggest railway in every respect . . . we want to make our big undertaking the undertaking of the country".

This new attitude soon made itself felt out on the line. In July 1893 one train in each direction between Paddington and Snow Hill consisted of all-corridor stock, the first such train in the country. Improvements in speed were to follow, with a pilot scheme in the summer of 1898, when the first non-stop train between Paddington and Snow Hill took 2 hours 27 minutes, an average speed of 52.7mph. "This train however – a summer tourist express for Wales – was hardly intended for local traffic, but the acceleration paved the way for an important improvement that took place the following summer" (Railway Magazine, December 1901). This was a non-stop express specifically for Birmingham, leaving Paddington at 2.10pm, taking 2 hours 25 minutes and conveying a slip coach for Leamington.

The LNWR had already sensed that the Great Western was rousing itself, so it ran extra trains between Euston and New Street from 1895, but without speeding up the service. Their immediate response to the 2.10pm express, in July 1899, was a new summer-dated 2.35pm from Euston, which took 2 hours 15 minutes to New Street, with a stop at Rugby.

As the new century dawned, competition was stiffening and passengers on both routes had an improving service. However, time-table planners were still firmly entrenched in the nineteenth century. The fastest trains on both routes were isolated examples. Regular clock-face timings, with a uniform pattern of stops, were confined to a few of the busier suburban lines. They simply did not occur with long distance trains. In 1901, the best Great Western train, the 9.30am from Snow Hill, took 2 hours 23 minutes non-stop. With an average speed of 54.2mph it was the second fastest train on their system. Despite the transformation taking place on the GWR, the average time and speed for the other ten daily trains was 3 hours 16 minutes and 39.5mph – reckless for Tyrrell, no faster than in 1852 and totally inadequate for a new century. The LNWR performed only slightly better, with eight trains down from Euston averaging 2 hours 46 minutes, trundling along at 41mph. As the "Railway Magazine" (December 1901) pointed out, it was possible to travel by the 5.30pm Midland Railway express from St.Pancras and, with a change at Leicester, still be in New Street by 8.39pm – 138½ miles at 43.9mph and in less time than by the slowest trains of either conventional route.

Churchward's new "Saints" and "Stars" quickly proved themselves as express locos. Despite their use on Birmingham trains, no substantial improvements to the Great Western service as a whole could take place until the route had been shortened and the congested approaches to Snow Hill eased. As well as a completely new section of line, this included quadrupling the track on the northern and southern approaches to Snow Hill, building a new suburban station at Moor Street, and rebuilding Snow Hill itself. This major work, with its inevitable disruption to traffic, took six years, starting in 1906.

Francis Webb was Locomotive Superintendent of the LNWR from 1871 until 1903. He had been responsible for many successful loco designs, such as the "Dreadnought" and "Jumbo" express passenger types. As traffic grew and trains lengthened, the size and power of his locos did not grow in proportion, causing most Anglo-Scottish expresses to be double-headed. Even some of the Birmingham trains, although lighter, were often piloted from Euston to Coventry, more out of habit than necessity. An observer ("Railway Magazine" September 1902) described how the 9.20am ex-Euston frequently received this treatment, even with a train of only 180 tons.

Webb's successor, George Whale, soon produced powerful

A "Star" in the twilight of its career, still hauling an express passenger train, though hardly on its normal route. No.4061 "Glastonbury Abbey" with the 2.10pm from Birmingham Snow Hill to Wolverhampton Low Level (formed out of the 10.00am ex-Paddington) on 23rd September 1956. Sunday engineering work caused this train to be diverted from the main line, via Handsworth Junction, Old Hill and the 'Bumble Hole' to join the route from Stourbridge to Wolverhampton at Netherton (Blower's Green). The train is seen climbing through the Black Country wilderness between Windmill End and Baptist End on the Bumble Hole line. *(Michael Mensing)*

Churchward designed the first British class of goods locomotive to have a 2-8-0 wheel arrangement in 1903. Over half a century later, on 4th June 1958, a member of this numerous and successful 2800 Class – No.2818 – passes through Acocks Green & South Yardley. The train is on the northbound fast line and the lamp headcode shows that this is a fitted freight, ie; the braking system is continuous throughout the train and can be applied to every vehicle, as in all passenger trains. Modernisation has only partially arrived; the new enamel sign indicating where 6 car dmus should stop is overshadowed by a gas lamp, dating from the rebuilding of the station in 1907.

(Michael Mensing)

The eye-catching poster issued to publicise the introduction of the 2 Hour expresses between New Street and Euston in 1905.

new types, the 4-4-0 "Precursor" of 1904 and 4-6-0 "Experiment" of 1906. The immediate success of the Precursors – the prototype hauled a 380-ton train between Crewe and Rugby at speeds up to 67mph – meant that, on the Birmingham line, double heading could be abolished and the service recast. The target of two hours between New Street and Euston had been almost within reach for a while, some trains attaining 2 hours 5 minutes in the 1902 time-table. It could now be met, and not just by one train. Beginning on 1st March 1905, four trains each way completed the journey in two hours non-stop. Seventeen other trains, nine southbound and eight northbound, were not non-stop but took only slightly longer. Some trains worked through to/from Wolverhampton. The attractive publicity poster showing eight Precursors, each beneath a clock face, was a new departure in railway art, more eye-catching and less ornate than many earlier examples. The LNWR issued more postcards than any other railway and the new service was marked by the issue of a full colour set of six, depicting loco and train. The cards were in a perforated strip so that they could be posted individually. Complete 'trains', one of which features in the colour section of this book, are now much sought after. This was now the premier service of the 'Premier Line', claimed at the time to be faster and more frequent than any other which connected cities over 100 miles apart.

W. L. Steel's "History of the London & North Western Railway" of 1914 gives a view of the new service, and of the rivalry with the GWR. It is unintentionally amusing and heavily biased:–

" . . . *there was the prospect looming ahead of increased competition at another important part of the system, for in this session (1905) the Great Western Railway lodged a Bill in Parliament seeking powers to construct a line greatly shortening its route between London and Birmingham and the West Midlands; and having successfully passed through Parliament, this Bill received the Royal Assent on 11th July. Before this Bill was passed, however, the London and North-Western gave the Great Western a foretaste of what it might expect should it be rash enough to challenge the North-Western's proverbial supremacy in the Midland Metropolis, for on 1st March the London and North-Western services between London and Birmingham were revolutionised, and four trains – in each direction - were placed on the service, doing the journey in 2 hours without a stop.*"

The LNWR enjoyed a monopoly of the fastest link with London for five years. In February 1910, anticipating completion of the GWR cut-off, the company provided an additional train, intended as the icing on the cake for the ever-increasing army of business travellers. This was the "City to City" express, starting at Wolverhampton (7.50am), calling at New Street (8.20) and Coventry (8.40), then running non-stop to London Broad Street (arr.10.30). This North London Railway terminus, alongside the Great Eastern's Liverpool Street, was very near the City of London's commercial and financial district, the heart of what was then the British Empire. The northbound train left Broad Street at 5.25pm, using the slow lines as far as Willesden, where it called to pick up any passengers who had caught a connecting train out of Euston at 5.20pm, arriving at New Street at 7.41pm. The "City to City" was the first train in Britain to cater specifically for the needs of the restless business executive on the move. One compartment was fitted out as an office, with a typist whose services were free of charge. There was a desk at which to work, revolving armchairs and a supply of specially headed notepaper. The typist was also a stenographer – taking notes in shorthand which she would later type in longhand – and work not completed by her on arrival at Broad Street could be delivered to its passenger in the City during the day or made ready for him to collect on the evening train. The train normally consisted of just four carriages, about 160 tons, including a refreshment vehicle for breakfast out and dinner return. The new Precursors were too heavy for the North London Line, so one of Webb's 4-4-0 four-cylinder compound engines was used when the service began, No.1918 "Renown". In 1908 it had been converted to a two-cylinder simple engine and fitted with a larger boiler. The "City to City" was a dedicated train, where neither the loco nor passenger stock was used for any other purpose. This innovative train, serving the predecessors of today's mobile phone and lap top computer users, was a victim of the service cuts of the First World War, running for the last time on Friday 19th February 1915.

The last major improvement to the New Street-Euston service before the outbreak of war was the addition of a specially adapted slip carriage for Coventry passengers, attached to the 8.40am and 6.55pm expresses from Euston. Unlike conventional slip coaches, passengers were not confined to it for the whole journey because it had a corridor connection, enabling them to use the restaurant car. Passage between slip coach and the rest of the train was via the slip guard's compartment. Prior to the act of slipping, the corridor was sealed with two doors, one at the end of the main train and one at the head of the slip coach.

The LNWR 2 hour expresses had been introduced as soon as the right locos became available. The GWR had had the right locos, the Saints, since 1902, but their expresses were not "rash enough to challenge" the LNWR until 1910, when the Aynho cut-off line was opened. This line runs from Aynho Junction, south of Banbury, to a point on what is now plain line but was then a junction with a Great Central connecting line at Ashenden, north of the present Haddenham & Thame Parkway station. It reduced the distance between Snow Hill and Paddington from 129¼ to 110¾ miles, as trains no longer had to go the Great Way Round via Oxford and Reading. *"The new line passes near Lord Jersey's country seat, and traverses a fine hunting country"* (Railway Magazine, December 1906). It opened on 1st July 1910. (It is curious how many major developments on the Great Western officially began on July 1st, whatever the year or day of the week. The first significant acceleration of the Birmingham trains (1899), opening of the North Warwickshire Line (1908) and the opening of Moor Street station (1909) are just a few among many instances.)

The first 2 hour express left Paddington at 9.10am hauled by No.2916 "Saint Benedict", with a load of almost 350 tons. Coaches were slipped at Princes Risborough and Leamington, there was a stop at High Wycombe and slack running at 40mph over the new line whilst it settled. Prolonged running at 75mph over favourable stretches meant that the train was only two minutes late into Snow Hill. VIPs aboard included the Lord Mayor of Birmingham and the Mayors of Aston Manor (separate from the city until 1911) Dudley, Leamington, Smethwick and Wolverhampton. The new service generated another attractive poster, featuring Star No.4013 "Knight of Saint Patrick".

Trains on both routes were slowed to 2½ hours and pruned in number during the First World War. After that war 2¼ hours was the norm, with the 2 hour service restored in October 1921. By 1925 the 7.10pm Paddington-Snow Hill-Shrewsbury was timed at 51 minutes start to stop between Princes Risborough and

Leamington, an average speed of 62mph, making it the fastest scheduled train in Britain. During 1935, the GWR centenary year, "The Bristolian" reduced the time between Paddington and Temple Meads to a fastest ever 1hour 45minutes. The Birmingham line from Paddington was 8 miles shorter than that to Bristol. By the winter of 1937-8 there was pressure upon the GWR to match the Bristol timings with those to Birmingham. Investigations found that 1¾ hours would be possible with a "King", hauling a maximum load of 300 tons. This was not followed up and the Great Western lost the initiative. The LMS speeded up one of its 2 hour expresses, by five minutes, in September 1935 and by 1938, the centenary of the Euston-Birmingham route, the LMS was running three trains from Euston to New Street (11.30am, 2.25pm and 5.50pm) in 115 minutes.

The London-Birmingham trains, by both routes, were fewer and slower during the Second World War. Timings and frequencies were not restored to pre-war levels until after 1947.

By 1910 the style of the Great Western's poster was simpler but just as eye-catching.

Cross Country and Suburban through Warwickshire
Great Western . . .

Nowadays, Birmingham New Street is the hub through which most of Britain's cross country trains pass. Such trains share three characteristics – they are generally fast, they cover long distances and they avoid London.

By 1900 the national rail network was virtually complete but an important cross country link still missing was the Great Western's own main line between Birmingham and Bristol. The company had wanted to build such a line in the 1840s, but had been thwarted in its ambitions by the Midland Railway. The only practical way between the two cities was along the main line of the Midland, via the Lickey Incline.

At the end of the nineteenth century the GWR was at last able to contemplate building its Bristol line. An important event which set things in motion was a meeting at Henley in 1893, as a result of which a Birmingham North Warwickshire and Stratford-upon-Avon Railway (BNW) was proposed. It was to be an independent route between Birmingham and Stratford via Henley-in-Arden. The Birmingham terminus would be at Moor Street, with no physical connection with the Great Western. There were to be five sections with gradients as steep as 1:51 or more, the steepest at 1:40. Tunnels and bridges near Moor Street would have severely disrupted life for local residents. The first three stations were to be sited within two miles of the terminus - easy prey to tramway competition. At the Stratford end the line would be linked to the East & West Junction Railway, a single track route which ran to Blisworth, on the Birmingham-Euston line. The Act consenting to the building of the BNW in this form was passed in August 1894.

At first the Great Western had little interest in the line and could see nothing to its own benefit in associating with it. It built the north loop at Hatton in 1897 as the first small step in a route to Bristol, still not fully appreciating that the BNW would be even more direct. The Great Central was more alert and full of ambition. Its main line from the East Midlands to London Marylebone was under construction and it began to flirt with the idea of its own service between London and Birmingham, via Stratford-upon-Avon. It would need to use the BNW north of Stratford and the East & West Junction as far east as Woodford Halse, where it was to join the Marylebone line. The Great Central offered to upgrade and double the poverty stricken EWJ's single track railway. This London-Birmingham route would have been about 117 miles long, 12 miles shorter than the GWR.

The Great Western woke up and opposed this plan vigorously, on the flimsy grounds that the BNW was not needed because Henley was already served by the GWR branch from Kingswood. The Great Central had to withdraw, as it needed the Great Western's co-operation over shared tracks in the London area to gain access to Marylebone. The BNW abandoned the idea of an independent route in 1899, favouring instead a link with the GWR at Tyseley. Powers to build the line were transferred to the GWR in July 1900. Amendments the following year formally scrapped the separate route into Moor Street and the link with the EWJ at Stratford. The new route was to be known as the North Warwickshire Line (NWL) probably because, although in the west of the county, it passes through the country of the North Warwickshire Hunt.

The NWL by itself would not have completed the new route to Bristol. Two single track branches, from Hatton in the east and Honeybourne in the south, met at Stratford. The whole line through to Honeybourne, from Bearley on the Hatton branch, was converted to double track, with improved alignment for faster running. Stations at Wilmcote, Long Marston, Milcote and Honeybourne were all rebuilt and given new platforms. South of Honeybourne a new railway was built, via Broadway, to Cheltenham, with easy curves for fast running and only one gradient of any consequence, half a mile at 1:108 falling into Cheltenham. This main line, often referred to as the Honeybourne Line, opened in 1906. Doubling of the line from Bearley to Honeybourne was completed in 1907. The North Warwickshire Line, 17³/4 miles between Tyseley and the junction at Bearley, opened to goods traffic in December 1907 and to passengers in 1908 - on July 1st. The line was aligned for express running up to 75mph; the route to Bristol was now complete.

Construction of the North Warwickshire had begun almost three years earlier, on 5th September 1905, at Henley. It was here, around the area where the station was to be built, that the contractor, C.J.Wills, established his base. For almost three years, up to 500 navvies were camped at Henley in the wooden huts of the shanty town. Here too was the makeshift engine shed. There were 23 locos used during construction, all but one were 0-4-0 saddle tanks. All ran on the contractor's undulating track at first, although the 'permanent way' was laid as soon as possible. The line used 11 steam navvies, which could each scoop up a ton of spoil in one bite.

Although less than perfect, this photograph shows part of the North Warwickshire Line under construction, near Hall Green. A horse is hauling a contractor's truck in the foreground gloom, with a steam navvy in the distance. By the early twentieth century railways were universally seen as 'a good thing', bringing all sorts of benefits unknown in earlier times. Would the owner of the greenhouse agree?

(courtesy of Birmingham Central Library)

Wood End, formerly Wood End Platform, with a southbound train on 25th March 1965. The spoil from this cutting was taken through the tunnel to form the embankment on the other side. *(Peter Shoesmith)*

During construction two places proved troublesome. The embankment south of Yardley Wood consists of gravel spoil from the cutting between Tyseley and Spring Road. As it was transferred from cutting to embankment during a period of very wet weather in the winter of 1906 it became saturated and very unstable. The embankment sides tended to bulge outwards, so a thin layer of heavy slag was applied to ease the problem. The only tunnel is at Wood End, 175 yards long. It was begun from the south side only. Spoil from the cutting at the north end was needed for the embankment at the south end. It made sense to begin the cutting only when the tunnel was nearing completion so that the spoil could be transferred through it, rather than over the hill. In August 1906, with work well advanced, a ventilator shaft was constructed, over 12 metres long. The following week, after a partial collapse of the tunnel, the shaft was the only escape route for men working at the face.

The stations at Tyseley, Hall Green, Shirley, Earlswood Lakes, Danzey and Henley were all provided with 500 foot long platforms. The lesser stations at Spring Road, Yardley Wood, Grimes Hill, Wood End and Wootton Wawen were all 'Platforms', a Great Western label for stops that offered more facilities than halts but fewer than most stations. As a rule they were staffed, at least part time, and accepted parcels traffic.

The new Birmingham engine shed, at Tyseley, replaced the smaller one at Bordesley. It was built partly to cater for the extra traffic that the North Warwickshire Line was expected to generate. It was a double roundhouse and opened in 1908 with an allocation of 70 locomotives. There was also a repair and lifting shop, with inspection pits on all twelve roads. The coaling stage was sited between tracks running from both roundhouses, so that locos could be coaled up from either side. The coaling stage survives intact but the site of Tyseley shed is now occupied by the Birmingham Railway Museum.

Events after the opening of the NWL were low key. After waiting so long for the main line to Bristol, the GWR provided just one long distance express per day. This linked Wolverhampton with Penzance, the ancestor of "The Cornishman". By 1911 there were three expresses each way between Birmingham and Bristol, the fastest taking a leisurely 135 minutes for the 99 miles. The number of regular cross country trains was never great, but this line really came into its own as the main holiday route from the Midlands to Devon and Cornwall, something which could not have been foreseen by those who had first wanted it in the 1840s.

The local service was also modest. South of Tyseley there were sporadic and infrequent bus services. Estate agents recognised the potential of the area and housing development quickly followed the opening of the line, particularly in Hall Green. The absence of tramway competition was a missed opportunity to establish a frequent regular interval service of the sort which was then proving so successful on the Harborne and Four Oaks lines out of New Street. Instead, local trains were modest both in quantity and size. Most were worked by rail motors. Only in the last quarter of the twentieth century was the local service developed to become frequent and regular, especially between Birmingham and Shirley, which now (1997) has trains at twenty minute intervals.

London & North Western ...

The LNWR and Midland were both developing cross country services in the early years of the century, although they often consisted of through carriages, or even a single carriage, rather than a complete train. In October 1910, for instance, journeys between the North-West, Birmingham and South Coast were made easier by the use of through carriages between Manchester London Road (dep.10am) and Bournemouth (arr.4.07pm). This called for smart work and close co-operation between the LNW and Midland at New Street, where just 10 minutes (11.53am-12.03pm) were allowed for transfer of the stock from the LNW train to a Midland restaurant car express, which would reach Bournemouth via the Somerset & Dorset Line. A mere 7 minutes were allowed for the northbound transfer at New Street. This service later developed into a through train, the ancestor of the "Pines Express". By 1925 it was a complete train, rather than through carriages, and its routeing through Birmingham was interesting. The southbound train arrived at the Midland side of the station, but via the Stour Valley Line. It left via the Camp Hill Line. The northbound train arrived at the Midland side of the station via the West Suburban Line. It left along the Grand Junction, via Aston and Bescot.

In 1910 it was also possible to travel in through carriages between Manchester and Bournemouth via Birmingham Snow Hill and Oxford, courtesy of the LNWR, GWR and London & South Western. However, the northbound carriages arrived at Crewe at 3.55pm *but at this point there is an irritating wait until 4.34pm, when the train is joined onto a LNWR train, arriving at Manchester at 5.28pm* (Railway Magazine, August 1910).

Since the 1960s this North-West – South Coast cross country route has developed enormously. Present day trains are normally routed via New Street, Coventry, Oxford, Reading and Winchester. On a normal weekday (1997) eight High Speed Trains in each direction complete the journey between New Street and Bournemouth in 3 hours 34 minutes southbound, slightly less northbound.

In July 1908 a short connection was opened between the Great Western and LNW lines at Leamington East, a simple operation as the two companies' Leamington stations were virtually 'back to back'. For two summers it was used by a new cross country train which was not a success. Operated jointly by the Great Western and Great Eastern, it ran between Cardiff General and Yarmouth Vauxhall, via the Honeybourne Line, Hatton, Leamington East Junction, Rugby and Peterborough.

The LNWR served Leamington with direct trains to Coventry and Rugby. In October 1908, in conjunction with the Midland, a through service of two trains each way began, linking Leamington with Leicester and Nottingham, via Coventry. [With good connections to/from Leamington, there is now an hourly service between Coventry, Leicester, Nottingham and Lincoln, a far cry from the two trains on offer in 1908.] In the summer of 1909, one of the 2 hour expresses, the 6.55pm from Euston, slipped a coach at Rugby for Leamington (arr.8.47pm). Meanwhile, a short distance to the south, the Great Western station at Leamington had been the subject of complaints since at least 1898. The shabby wooden shacks were not in keeping with either the image of a select spa town or the improving Great Western. The down-at-heel appearance is obvious from the

The rebuilding at Leamington Spa begins to take shape, 22nd March 1937. On the left is a local train for Birmingham. The original part of the main line platform for Birmingham is low indeed.
(courtesy of Birmingham Post & Mail)

photograph, which was taken many years later, in the summer of 1937, when new station buildings were at last being provided. This station was completed in 1939 and it now has a certain period charm.

Of the suburban services in Warwickshire before 1914, the busiest was the shortest, between New Street and Harborne. A northern section of what is now the Birmingham Cross City Line, between New Street and Four Oaks, was also busy. There were 7 trains in each direction on opening in 1862, rising to 15 in 1870 and 30 by 1900 (and 64 in 1997). In April 1900 the "Railway Magazine" commented:-

"The service is so good and so well arranged that it is not uncommon for those who reside on the branch, and have their business in the city, to go to and fro for their meals. These are season ticket holders, who get good value for their money!"

For the summer of 1911 this line even had its own holiday express, in one direction only! The train from Llandudno to New Street (arr.3.16pm) worked through to Four Oaks.

Each railway had its own house style. Two distinguishing features of the LNWR were the large platform lamps, the station name painted in the glass and, on many suburban platforms, signs indicating where 1st, 2nd and 3rd class passengers should wait, as in the photograph taken at Erdington. Second class was abolished on the LNWR at the end of 1911 and on the GWR in the Midlands in 1910 – on July 1st, of course.

Erdington, looking towards Sutton Coldfield, about 1910. There is a sense of tidiness and unchanging order here, almost as though the station would last in this form for centuries. The signs show the different classes of passenger where to wait on the platforms. Wicker pigeon baskets and a travelling trunk are in evidence, and even the fire bucket is labelled and numbered. The lamps are standard LNWR, with the station name painted on the glass. The train is passing the signal, where the Chester Road distant arm is also painted red, not yet yellow. The skyscraper signal for Birmingham bound trains – seemingly cut in two by the locomotive exhaust – is a trifle extravagant, even for the LNWR.
(Lens of Sutton)

. . . and Midland.

Until 1941 there were two 'circle' services based on New Street, one LNW, one Midland. LNW circle trains leaving the Euston end of New Street ran via Aston and Perry Barr, on what had originally been the Grand Junction main line, the first railway into Birmingham in 1837. At Perry Barr they turned south onto the Soho Loop, through Handsworth Wood and, via Soho East and South junctions, gained the Stour Valley Line back into New Street. More trains worked this route in the other direction, anti-clockwise. Circle trains were confined to the peak hours, plus a lunchtime working. Other local trains - to and from Sutton, Walsall (by two routes) or Wolverhampton, provided a much more frequent service at all 8 circle stations. LNW circle trains ceased in May 1941 and both stations on the Soho Loop were closed at the same time.

The Midland circle trains were also confined to the peaks, plus a lunchtime working. They ran over both the main line approaches to the city from the south. To the east was the Camp Hill Line, the original 1840 main line of the Birmingham & Gloucester Railway; to the west lay the Birmingham West Suburban Railway, a single track branch running north from King's Norton which the Midland doubled and opened through to New Street via Five Ways in 1885. Circle trains began as soon as Lifford Curve opened in 1892 (on July 1st!). The curve completed the circle, just north of the junction of the two main lines at King's Norton. There were 11 stations on the Midland circle; the last to open was Hazelwell (1903), the first to close was Church Road (1925). All stations were served by other local trains between New Street and Redditch, Evesham and Bromsgrove, all via Barnt Green. Midland circle trains were

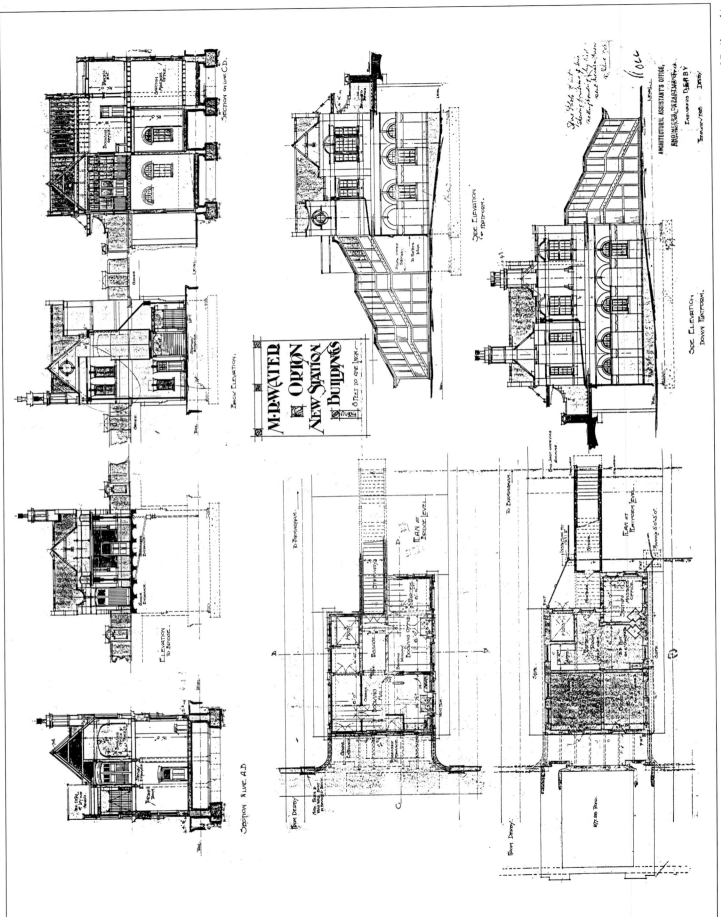

(courtesy of Railtrack)

The Midland Railway re-built Water Orton station in 1908 and, as these plans show, the result was very satisfying.

Johnson 4-4-0 No.405 passes the box at Halesowen Junction, Longbridge, with a Bristol express about 1905.   *(Don Powell collection)*

withdrawn in January 1941, and all stations on the Camp Hill Line were closed at the same time. In more recent times, after thirteen very lean years with virtually no local passenger trains (1965-78), the West Suburban is now part of the Cross City Line.

The Birmingham main lines of the LNWR and Great Western were built as links with London; the Midland route was not. The railway had been operating cross country services on its Bristol-Birmingham-Derby main line since the 1840s, so it had developed a large number of through trains and through carriages to a wide variety of destinations long before the other two fully appreciated how useful such workings could be. There was even a through service to Swansea via Brecon, thanks to running rights over the Great Western between Stoke Works Junction (south of Bromsgrove), Worcester and Hereford. An article in "Railway Magazine" (April 1910), itemised some of the possibilities for through travel. I have summarised the northbound daytime cross country trains then running. All times quoted are departures from Bristol. Names written before the time are the originating stations for some through carriages which were attached en route; names written after the time are the final destination of at least one through carriage. All trains, except the 2.10pm, served Bristol, Birmingham and Derby.

	8.05am	Sheffield, York
	8.55am	
	9.45am	Sheffield, Bradford, Leeds, Manchester, York, Newcastle
Bournemouth	10.45am	Leeds, Bradford, Edinburgh, Glasgow
Bournemouth	12.20pm	Leeds, Bradford, Manchester, Sheffield, York
Southampton	12.53pm	Sheffield, York
	2.10pm	to Nottingham, not Derby
Kingswear	2.17pm	Leeds, Bradford, Manchester, Sheffield
Bournemouth/	3.25pm	Great Malvern, Manchester,
		Halifax, Heysham, York
Southampton	4.40pm	Heysham (Belfast Boat Express)
Bournemouth	4.52pm	Leeds, Bradford, Manchester
	6.08pm	(connections at Derby for
Edinburgh		and Glasgow)
	7.00pm	Leeds, Newcastle
	7.55pm	Leeds, Newcastle, Edinburgh, Glasgow

East of Birmingham all trains had been routed via Whitacre, junction of the line to Nuneaton and Leicester, as well as of the little used branch to Hampton-in-Arden, the original main line between Derby and London. A five-mile line was opened in 1909, between the junctions at Water Orton and Kingsbury, which by-passed Whitacre, speeding up expresses between Birmingham and Derby by at least five minutes.

The Great Western, LNWR and Midland all built attractive suburban stations in Warwickshire. Some Great Western buildings survive in more or less original condition and are busy with commuters, as at Tyseley and Shirley. LNWR examples are few, but must include Sutton Coldfield. Of the few ex-Midland Railway suburban stations in Warwickshire, only one remains open, at Water Orton. It was rebuilt at the same time as the direct line by-passing Whitacre. The architect's drawings (Derby, February 1908) show a delightful building in the Arts & Crafts style. The street entrance led into the booking hall and a staircase gave access to the island platform. The station gained local fame in recent years because of the care lavished on it by the staff. Trains were few, but those waiting for them could read a magazine, add pieces to a jigsaw or simply admire the flowers displayed in the many vases. Alas, the station is now unstaffed, and the platform buildings demolished - a small but attractive part of the local community has gone, replaced by a bare platform with its basic shelter.

Differing Moods at Birmingham New Street

The crowded footbridge at New Street, photographed about 1910 from the steps up to the Stephenson Street exit. Most people are heading towards the camera, suggesting the recent arrival of at least one crowded train. Above them all is the Number 3 Signal Box, signalman looking north and resting on a lever in the off position. Labour costs were cheap, so the enormous area of roof glass was still kept clean, a feature which declined noticeably in LMS days. The lower set of tie-bars were added to strengthen the roof support system during 1906-07. The originals above them are on steeper curves and appear more slender. The lighter area in the background shows Queen's Drive, the roadway separating the LNWR and Midland sides of the station. Alcohol abuse was a problem, not surprising given the price of the beer!

(Author's collection)

Renewed Precedent No.1666 "Ariadne" at Platform 2, Birmingham New Street, about 1903. This express passenger loco was built in 1891 and scrapped in 1925. It looks as though a wild barrow party has just finished, far too wild for this narrow island platform.

(Thomas Hinckley; Roger Carpenter collection)

The LNW side of New Street, looking towards Euston. The sun struggles to find a way through the grubby overall roof, 1933. (courtesy of Birmingham Post & Mail)

A superb night shot of "Prince of Wales" No.25725 with a train at New Street's Platform 3, 20th August 1938. In the days long before platform monitor screens, the LMS had inherited standard LNWR clock dials and fingerboards, slotted vertically into a wooden base when not required. (L. Hanson)

21

[Diary : Putting the Great back into the Western : Notes, War and Aftermath]

Diary

1910

February 1st – Wolverhampton-Birmingham New Street-London Broad Street service began.

April 1st – Heath Town closed.

July 1st – Second class accommodation withdrawn from all Great Western trains in the Birmingham area. This followed the practice of most other railways, begun by the Midland in 1875. An anomoly persisted throughout the country until the 1950s; passengers could only travel 1st or 3rd class. Third class became second, re-labelled 'standard' as recently as 1988.

July 1st – Aynho cut-off line opened.

1911

One of the hottest summers of the century. By this time some railways had developed "Passengers' Luggage in Advance" almost into an art form. A special train left New Street at 12.35am every night in the summer, consisting of eight vans of passengers' luggage bound for Rhyl, Bangor, Llandudno (2), Blackpool (2), Aberystwyth and Liverpool. This train connected with others at Crewe, where vans from Leicester and Leeds were added.

1912

Rebuilding of Birmingham Snow Hill completed.

May 1st – Bushbury station closed.

October 1st – LNWR began its own bus service between Hednesford and Brownhills.

December 1st – First LNWR platform ticket machines, at Wolverhampton High Level. The tickets cost one old penny (1d) and permitted access to the platforms for one hour. Revenue at the end of the first month was £43/7/8d (£43.38) from 10,412 tickets. The machines had cost £39/18/- (£39.90) so they had already made a profit! Nowadays the wheel has come full circle, most stations have open access; ticket barriers and platform tickets are endangered species.

1913

September 15th – Tickets barriers installed at Walsall, removing lengthy delays to trains whilst tickets were collected at the previous stopping station.

1914

January 7th – Birmingham Moor Street goods station opened.

August 10th – Coventry Loop Line opened.

1915

(Wartime closures – those lines and stations which subsequently re-opened marked *)

January 1st (ie; 31/12/14) – Lapworth-Henley branch closed to passengers; goods traffic confined to the short link between Henley's goods and passenger stations from the beginning of 1916; track lifted during the summer of 1917.

February 19th – Wolverhampton-Birmingham-London Broad Street business express withdrawn.

March – Oldbury and Stourbridge Town* branches closed to passengers.

May – Bradley & Moxley station closed. This was south of Bilston, near the present day Bradley Lane stop on Line 1 of the Midland Metro.

November 29th – Snow Hill to Dudley passenger service, plus Great Bridge (GWR) station closed.*

1916

January 1st – Birchills and Landywood halts closed. Princes End and Ocker Hill stations closed.

July 14th – Burlington Road Ordnance Depot opened on the Coventry Loop line.

1917

There was a whole batch of closures throughout the country on January 1st, (ie; services ceased at the end of 1916) in compliance with the demands of the military authorities.

GWR – Dunstall Park*, Daisy Bank*.

LNWR – Monmore Green, Pleck*, New Street-Worcester via Stourbridge.

Midland – New Street-Worcester-Hereford; Whitacre-Hampton-in-Arden.

1918

Track of Stratford & Moreton Tramway lifted for scrap, probably in March.

1919

March 3rd – Dunstall Park and Daisy Bank re-opened

April – Ordinary passenger service, Halesowen-Northfield withdrawn; Hunnington and Rubery closed.

May 1st – Stourbridge Town re-opened.

September 26th – October 5th – National Rail Strike.

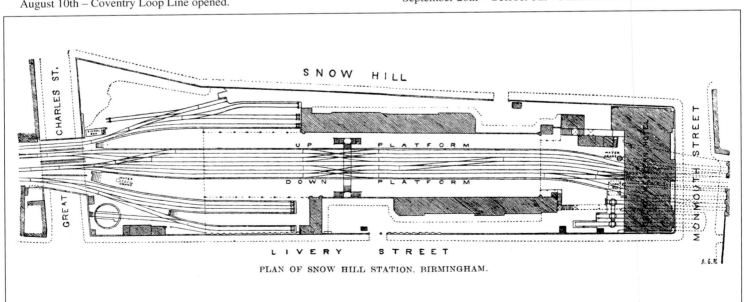

PLAN OF SNOW HILL STATION, BIRMINGHAM.

The second station at Birmingham Snow Hill, which had become very cramped by the time this plan appeared in the "Railway Magazine" in 1901.

Putting the Great back into the Western

The first station at Birmingham Snow Hill opened with the line in October 1852. It was a large temporary wooden shed that lasted until 1871, after which it was re-erected as a carriage shed at Didcot.

The 120 bedroom Great Western Hotel was a familiar Birmingham landmark for over a century, although it accepted paying guests for less than half that time. It opened in 1863 and was improved when the second station was built. In conjunction with the building of the third station in 1906-12 it was converted into office accommodation and a wide new arch was let into the Colmore Row facade, creating the main passenger entrance into the new station.

The second Snow Hill station had an overall roof spanning the main platforms and the suburban bays alongside Livery Street. It was not a bad design, just ordinary. By 1900 it was outmoded and the main difficulty was the cramped site, at a time when all types of traffic were increasing. The main line to Bristol, which would attract yet more long distance and suburban traffic, was already in prospect.

There were just two through platforms, with two more through lines for freight, three suburban bays at the northern end of the station and none at the southern. The sidings at the northern end, on the up side, were used mainly for stabling slip coaches to be attached to Paddington trains. These were slipped at Hatton (for Stratford), Warwick, Banbury, Oxford and Reading and in 1901 every train, except the 5.45pm, carried at least one slip coach. 'Slipping' from trains from Snow Hill ceased in 1916.

The "Railway Magazine" for March 1901 provided some statistics. There were about 6,000 season ticket holders using the station every day, most of their commuter trains consisting of close-coupled 'twins' made up of two brake thirds, two thirds, two composites and one second. Twenty-seven sets of 'twins' covered the Birmingham area suburban traffic. The staff, from Stationmaster Herring (1897-1921) down to the most junior porter, numbered about 240. Up to four hundred trains passed through the station every day. Between midnight and 5am the freight roads echoed to an almost continuous procession of goods trains, a factor which diminished the popularity of the Great Western Hotel and led to its closure. As well as the usual trains of house coal and those supplying the needs of the industrial Black Country, the Great Western supplied the West Midlands with all its fruit, vegetables and flowers that had originated in Devon and Cornwall.

The stabling of carriages was a serious problem, particularly in the summer peaks . . .

"So congested has the traffic become, that there is no longer any accommodation for rolling stock of any description that becomes quiescent; and consequently the formation of all trains has to take place at Bordesley Junction and Small Heath, two miles from Snow Hill, and in spite of the recent introduction of five fresh sidings at Bordesley, more space is still needed to cope satisfactorily with excursion traffic, which during the summer months is exceptionally heavy, as many as two hundred extra coaches being required."

(Railway Magazine, March 1901)

The main platforms, which had scissors crossings midway, were just 450 feet long, fine in 1871 but totally inadequate by 1900. A sum of £341,693 (the Great Western did not believe in rough estimates!) was authorised for the complete reconstruction of Snow Hill station in November 1902. The new station was designed by Walter Armstrong, the Great Western's New Works Engineer. Preliminary work began in September 1905 and in earnest the following spring. It was completed in 1912. It was impossible to expand the width of the site, confined by Livery Street and Snow Hill itself. The only way was along, like excess toothpaste squeezed from a tube, over Great Charles Street and towards Wolverhampton. A wide new bridge over Great Charles Street carried the platforms. These now consisted of two enormous islands, giving the station four through passenger roads as well as the two for freight. The longest through platform, numbered 5 and 6 (down main) extended to 1,215 feet; the shortest 11-12 (up relief) was 970 feet. There were originally scissors crossings midway along the two main platforms, so that they could each serve two trains at a time when the need arose. Bays were let into the north ends of each island, providing four suburban platforms, numbered 3, 4, 9 and 10. What is obvious from the photographs and the plans reproduced here (signed by Armstrong and dated 15th March 1909) is that with this station Birmingham gained one of its best twentieth century buildings. All buildings should work well and be pleasing to the eye; Snow Hill was successful on both these counts.

One feature which attracted criticism before the station was even built was the roof. A contemporary magazine "The Owl" became very agitated when it learnt that the roof would not be completely covered in:-

"How will such a station represent the importance of the town? . . . Such a station ought not to represent a wayside appearance, a sort of magnified Hockley, Vauxhall or Saltley . . . Looking around the kingdom we see at once that there is not a railway station of first importance on any line or in any large town where the covered-in principle has not been adhered to. Whatever may be the economic advantage attaching to the proposal of the Great Western directors it means a second rate status for their chief provincial station . . ."

As the building neared completion, it became increasingly obvious that "The Owl" was mistaken. The ridge and furrow roof covered the four main platforms, from the booking hall to Great Charles Street. The absence of glazing over the freight lines allowed extra light to enter and surplus steam to escape.

The platform buildings had four colours of brickwork, Staffordshire blue at the base and red above the bottom of the window arches. The bricks between the base and the window sills were glazed chocolate, with cream glazed bricks above. The brickwork was complemented by buff-coloured terracotta around and above the window arches and along the top frieze. Beneath the platforms, hidden from public view, were areas for storage and a large depot for the collection and delivery of parcels. Because the site sloped down to the north, these areas were of one storey at the Paddington end, but two for most of the remainder. This whole area had required the excavation of over ten thousand cubic metres of earth, as the earlier stations had no such 'underground' parts. The platforms and running lines were not at ground level at all, but carried on an immense raft of concrete and asphalt in a steel framework. Over 6,000 tons of steel was used, the largest girders having a length of 89 feet 8 inches (c.27 metres) and a weight of 59 tons. The steel was all supplied by the main contractor, E.C.& J.Keay Ltd., from their foundry at James Bridge, Darlaston, all delivered by rail and erected without interruption to the train services.

The two manual signalboxes were replaced by two power boxes, each with a frame of miniature levers. Modern technology only went so far – the signals they controlled were still lower quadrant semaphores. The north box, perched on top of a narrow steel frame and hemmed in by running lines, had 189 levers and 35 spares. It opened in 1909. The smaller south box (75 levers and 21 spares) followed in 1913. Power was supplied at 5,000 volts, reduced to 140 volts "at the railway company's sub-station by static transformers". The signals and points could all be operated by a simple flick of the signalman's wrist. Interlocking

Snow Hill's magnificent booking hall, when new. Notice the liveried coachman, the chauffeur and the advertisement promoting a day return fare to London for 8/6d. (42.5p).   *(courtesy of Kidderminster Railway Museum)*

of signalling and points was still mechanical, but their actual working was electical, meaning that it was as easy to work the most distant signal (620 yards from the box) or point (243 yards) as any just outside.

The booking hall had a curved glazed roof spanning 93 feet, 54 feet above the ground. It was also equipped with two German machines for the automatic printing of tickets, as required, using blank cards and dispensing with a large stock of pre-printed tickets. These were the first such machines used in Britain. Such progress was welcome but it might mean unemployment for some, as the "Railway Magazine" sensed - *"If such machines should become general, fewer booking clerks will be required"*. Two broad passages led from the booking hall to the wide staircases down to the platforms. Some of the suburban carriages of the time may have been 'twins' but Snow Hill possessed two

more twins, fondly remembered by those who knew this station. They were the clocks, mounted in oak cases, one in the booking hall, one above Platform 7.

Because of the congestion on the lines approaching Snow Hill, the rebuilding of the station was only the main part of a wider programme of improvements. There was still no room for the much needed suburban platforms at the southern end of Snow Hill, so a complete new station was built for this purpose at Moor Street. This terminus opened in 1909 with just an island platform. The platform buildings were a pleasing small scale reflection of those at Snow Hill. The side platform, with its back to the main line emerging from Snow Hill tunnel, had featured in the original plan, but was not built until 1930. Moor Street was also the starting point for southbound excursion trains, a considerable relief to Snow Hill.

A view of Snow Hill station from the top of the steps down to Platform 5. The rake of carriages standing at Platform 7 is painted in crimson lake. This livery was introduced in 1912 after a brief flirtation with all-over brown in 1909. The familiar chocolate and cream was restored in 1922. The card was not posted until 1931. *(Author's collection)*

It may seem that all the improvements at this time happened smoothly, as parts of a large and well co-ordinated rolling programme. This was only partly true. Sometimes there is a hint that events were improvised 'on the hoof', if not by the seat of the pants then at least on the back of an envelope. Moor Street station was a case in point. It was known that it would be needed for the North Warwickshire Line but it was not ready to open until a year after the line opened and even then it was barely serviceable, with unfinished buildings and no platform canopy. It was not completed until 1914. The line between Bordesley and Moor Street needed to be quadrupled, but work had barely begun when the station opened. Moor Street signal box, which controlled the adjacent main lines as well those within the station, opened in 1909. After just four years, when quadrupling was completed, it was replaced by a new box and removed for further use at Foxhall Junction, Didcot. The goods facilities at Bordesley were inadequate and more needed to be found, but only in 1909, when Moor Street was already open, did the Great Western make efforts to buy the land and property alongside for a new goods station. It opened on 7th January 1914. There was a 400 foot long loading platform - almost as long as the main platforms at the old Snow Hill - along which a rail-mounted 1-ton travelling crane roamed. Surface sidings could hold over 200 wagons and further sidings were located in the warehousing at

low level, reached by wagon turntables and hoists. These held up to 121 wagons. Stabling for the GWR cart horses was also at this level. As at Snow Hill, a lot of goods activity occurred underground, unknown to the majority of passengers above.

The main line across the city, between Olton and Handsworth Junction, was quadrupled in stages. The goods yards at Hockley were extended and modernised with the latest type of travelling crane, but the remodelled passenger station here was another victim of the railway's lack of space, as there was sufficient room for a platform face for only three of the four running lines - the down fast line (towards Wolverhampton) was denied. All stations on the newly quadrupled track were rebuilt, often with street level booking offices and island platforms, as at Small Heath and Acocks Green. This left the two track section in Snow Hill tunnel itself, on a gradient rising from Moor Street at 1:45. Widening of this section was impractical. The colossal cost and disruption would have meant demolition of the Great Western Arcade, full of high quality shops, which had been built over the former cutting in 1876 and, in effect, acted as the roof of the tunnel. Only the existence of Moor Street station, plus the experience of many years' smart tunnel working and astute time-tabling prevented this unavoidable narrowing of the main artery from clogging the whole system.

(text continues on page 28)

No.7915 "Mere Hall" is seen to advantage from this low angle, at the north end of Snow Hill's Platform 7, with the 17.28 to Knowle & Dorridge on 20th July 1964. My reference to the 24 hour clock is deliberate, as Snow Hill was the first station in the Midlands to use it on public time-tables, around 1962. The Staffordshire knot emblem on the bridge was adapted as the trade mark of E. C. & J. Keay of James Bridge, Darlaston (in Staffordshire until 1974), who supplied almost six thousand tons of steel for the station rebuilding.

(Robert Darlaston)

A posed photograph of Knowle before the quadrupling which took place in the twentieth century. The high signal is on 'wrong line' to give clearer vision to the train crew rounding the bend. The width between the tracks shows that this was once a broad gauge railway. Everything is in apple-pie order, June 1891.

(courtesy of Birmingham Post & Mail)

Mind The Gap. 2-6-2T No.3101 moves away from the platform edge on the traverser at Birmingham Moor Street, May 1957. The loco was one of just five belonging to the 3100 Class, 1938 rebuilds from the 3150 Class of 1907, with larger driving wheels and boiler pressure increased from 200 to 225lb./sq.".

(Robert Darlaston)

2-6-2 tank engine No.4146 (5100 Class) passing through Hockley on the platformless down fast line with a service for Dudley, 10th September 1959.

(Michael Mensing)

Meanwhile, across the city centre, plans were drawn up for the improvement of New Street station. This would involve converting the four suburban bays on the LNWR side into two long through platforms. The famous footbridge would cease to be a public right of way, as its use would be confined to rail passengers. It was to be replaced as a right of way by a new bridge across the station, approached from Stephenson Place by a subway. A large booking hall was to be built at the Stephenson Place entrance and the Queen's Hotel was to be altered and enlarged. A contract was placed and the work was due to take two years. What happened? The hotel was enlarged between 1915 and 1917, but all these proposals were outlined in a paragraph in the "Railway Magazine" of May 1914, and suggestions of this type were swept away by events later that summer.

LANGLEY GREEN AND ROOD END and OLDBURY (Motor Cars—One class only).—G.W.

Miles	Down. Week Days.	mrn	mrn	mrn	mrn	mrn	mrn	mrn	mrn	mrn	mrn	aft	aft	aft	aft	aft	aft	aft	aft	aft	aft	aft	aft
	Langley Green ‡ ..dep.	5 45	6 3	6 37	7 0	7 32	8 33	9 30	1034	1050	1142	1210	1227	1256	1 17	1e42	1s45	2 36	2 53	3 25	3 43	4 19	4 48
¾	Oldbury ....arr.	5 48	6 6	6 40	7 3	7 35	8 36	9 33	1037	1053	1145	1213	1230	1259	1 20	1e45	1s48	2 39	2 56	3 28	3 46	4 22	4 51

Down. Week Days—Continued.	aft	aft	aft	aft	aft	aft	aft	aft	aft
Langley Green ‡ ......dep.	5 40	6 31	6 56	7 16	7 36	8 29	8 48	9 30	9 45
Oldbury ....arr.	5 43	6 34	6 59	7 19	7 39	8 32	8 51	9 33	9 48

e Except Saturdays. *s* Saturdays only. ‡ Langley Green and Rood End.

STOURBRIDGE JUNCTION and STOURBRIDGE (Motor Cars—One class only).—G.W.—¾ mile.
Stourbridge Junction to Stourbridge at 6b35, 7 22, 8, 8 7, 8b30, 8 54, 9 8, 9 23, 9 38, 9 55, 10 6, 10 19, 10 45, 10 55, 11 14, and 11 25 mrn., 12 6, 12 36, 12 54, 1 17, 1 44, 2e1, 2s6, 2 20, 2 57, 3 14, 3 23, 3 35, 3 55, 4 6, 4 30, 4 54, 5 10, 5 43, 6 2, 6 14, 6 25, 6 45, 6 56, 7 21, 7 35, 7 45, 7 57, 8 11, 8 21, 8 45, 8 55, 9 20, 9 40, 9 55, 10 9, 10 43, 10 57, and 11 20 aft. SUNDAYS at 8 45, 8 58, 9 8, 11 5, and 11 35 mrn., 12 22, 2 57, 3 13, 3 28, 4 10, 4 35, 7 20, 7 42, 8 55, 9 5, 9 20, and 10 10 aft.
b 1st 2nd, and 3rd class. *e* Except Saturdays. *s* Saturdays only.

LAPWORTH and HENLEY-IN-ARDEN.—Great Western.

Miles	Down. Week Days.	mrn	m	m	m	aft	m	m	m
	Lapworth ....dep	7 8	9 17	1122	2 40	4 54	5 42	6 55	7 53
4¾	Henley-in-Arden ..arr.	7 20	9 27	1132	2 50	5 5	5 52	7 5	8 3

Mls	Up.	mrn	m	m	m	m	aft	m
—	Henley-in-Arden ..dep.	7 50	9 0	1015	1 30	4 30	5 20	7 20
4¾	Lapworth 74, 81 ..arr.	8 0	9 10	1025	1 40	4 40	5 30	7 30

m Motor Car, one class only.

DUDLEY PORT, PRINCES END, and WEDNESBURY.—London and North Western.

Miles	Up. Week Days. High Level,	mrn	mrn	aft	aft	aft
	Dudley Port ......dep	8 50	1022	1220	3 20	6 52
¾	Tipton	8 52	1025	1223	3 23	6 54
2	Princes End	8 55	1028	1226	3 26	6 57
3	Ocker Hill	8 58	1031	1229	3 29	7 0
3¾	Wednesbury 447 ..arr.	9 0	1035	1232	3 32	7 2

Miles	Down. Week Days.	mrn	mrn	aft	aft
	Wednesbury ....dep.	7 38	1052	1255	3 42
¾	Ocker Hill	7 41	1055	1258	3 45
1¾	Princes End	7 44	1058	1 1	3 48
3	Tipton 450	7 47	11 2	1 4	3 51
3¾	Dudley Port (H.L.) 447	7 49	11 4	1 6	3 53

HAMPTON BRANCH.
Midland.

Miles	Week Days.	mrn
	Hampton.......dep.	9 30
4½	Coleshill.......[579	9 40
6½	Whitacre 572, arr.	9 45

Mls		mrn
—	Whitacre......dep.	8 25
2	Coleshill...........	8 32
6½	Hampton 449..arr.	8 40

From Bradshaw's Railway Guide for April 1910. All these services closed during the First World War; only the Stourbridge line re-opened to passengers. *(courtesy of Robert Pearson)*

Notes, War and Aftermath

There were more station closures between 1910 and 1919 than in any earlier ten-year period. Not all of them could be blamed on the war. Tramways provided a frequent, reliable and cheap service; they were able to pick off inner city stations almost at will. Heath Town, near the Wolverhampton end of the Midland's less-than-prosperous line from Walsall, closed in 1910, while across the town centre, Bushbury succumbed in 1912. Could this have had anything to do with the fact that income from ticket sales at Bushbury for the whole of 1911 was £42, an average of less than £1 per week?

Selly Oak, Bournville and King's Norton are all busy today but during this period they remained open whilst losing many passengers to the trams. Forty-two trains in each direction ran between King's Norton and New Street six days a week, and the single fare was just 5½d (2p). This may seem adequate, but the new tramcars on the No.36 route to Cotteridge, with their terminus near the station, went to and fro at least double that number of times, for a fare of just 2d (1p).

As the railways were under government control during the war many minor lines and stations were closed by order of the military authorities to release men and, in some instances, to obtain the track for scrap. The subsequent fortunes of such lines varied considerably. The Lapworth-Henley trains were withdrawn and most of the track was lifted. The branches to Stourbridge Town and Oldbury were both busy but short. Perhaps someone in uniform looked at a map and decided that their many passengers could walk. Only the Stourbridge branch re-opened.

This was the least frequent and least used train in England! Whitacre in 1902, with the train for Coleshill and Hampton-in-Arden in the foreground. The loco is Johnson 0-6-0 No.2461 and the carriage is an elderly vehicle with guard's van and compartments for 1st,2nd and 3rd class passengers. This was before the Kingsbury cut-off opened, so the other train could have been heading for either the Leicester or Derby line.

(Chris Banks collection)

The branch between Whitacre and Hampton-in-Arden started life in 1839 as part of a main line between Derby and London. Inter-company hostilities, and the completion of a more direct route, led to its downgrading and singling by 1843, possibly the first main line in the world to receive this pre-Beeching treatment. Whitacre and Hampton were both well served by trains to other places; Coleshill, the only place with a station along the line, was better served by its main line station at Forge Mills. This branch went from nothing to nowhere. From the 1880s onwards the service consisted of one train a day and on most days there were more trains than passengers who wished to use them. Normally the single composite brake coach was hauled by an elderly 0-6-0 freight loco. This was the line's statutory 'Parliamentary' train which nobody seemed to know how to close, until wartime economies provided an excuse to put it out of its misery at the end of 1915. The daily goods service continued and, as the Second World War approached, the line briefly had a vital role to play . . .

Passenger services not closed by the war were affected by it and most local lines had fewer trains after 1915. Long distance passengers were also confronted by fewer and slower trains. The direct train to London Broad Street was axed by the LNWR in February 1915, but so were two trains down from Euston and one up. The schedule for the remaining 2 hour trains was increased, by 30 minutes for some. Cross country services such as the 8.40am and 4.35pm from New Street to Manchester, were axed. LNW restaurant cars were few, finally disappearing completely in April 1916. For those hoping to get away from it all, rail travel was actively discouraged. The August Bank Holiday period in 1915 saw few holiday excursions and no cheap fares. Early in 1916 the Great Western withdrew two trains between Paddington and Snow Hill, while those remaining were slowed by up to 10 minutes.

Despite, and in some cases, because of the war, improvements continued. Sometimes they were imperceptible, such as on the Wombourn line, where the GWR reported in 1916 that work was still progressing, but slowly, "consequent upon the shortage of labour and the difficulty in obtaining materials". The same year saw completion of the widening between Small Heath and Bordesley and the extension of the Birmingham Train Control System out to Banbury. In 1917 some 'works of national importance' were completed on the Great Western to cope with the great increase in freight movement brought on by the war. They included down goods loops between Bilston and Wednesbury and additional sidings at Hockley, Cradley, Swan Village and Halesowen.

The Coventry Loop Line opened on 10th August 1914, six days after the outbreak of war. It was a 3½ mile long double track freight route, for which powers were obtained in 1907, built to serve the needs of an expanding industrial area. (If only a greater number of modern industrial areas were directly served by rail!) There were goods depots and signal boxes at Gosford Green and Bell Green. The Royal Naval Ordnance Depot near the line, at Burlington Road was also rail connected. Heavy guns and sea mines were sent from here to the Grand Fleet.

The Birmingham Railway Carriage & Wagon Co., with access to the GWR main line via the down goods yard at Handsworth & Smethwick station, contributed to the war effort by supplying a hospital train, thousands of ammunition wagons, high explosive shells (25,000 in a single order, placed in 1915) and – from 1917 – no fewer than 93 aircraft, Handley Page bombers.

Metro-Cammell, then known as the Metropolitan Carriage, Wagon & Finance Co.Ltd., secured a government contract for building some of the first tanks, at the Old Park Works, Wednesbury and at another of its plants in Spon Lane, Oldbury, alongside the Stour Valley line.

Members of the St.John Ambulance Brigade and the Royal Army Medical Corps await the arrival of war wounded, Platform 5, Birmingham Snow Hill, c.1916. *(courtesy of Birmingham Post & Mail)*

Some time during the First World War, soldiers march out of New Street station, via Queen's Drive and along John Bright Street. A tram on the King's Heath via Leopold Street route stands at its terminus in Hill Street. *(courtesy of Birmingham Post & Mail)*

After the war, statistics emerged to be published in the "Railway Magazine" (March 1920). The number of large tanks (35 tons) forwarded by Metro-Cammell from Spon Lane between April 1918 and May 1919 was 2,202, sent mainly to the southern ports but also to "tankodromes" (sic) for storage in Dorset and Berkshire.

The Midland Railway in the Birmingham area transported *a large number of aircraft engines, 40,000 motor cycles, 500,000 bicycles, 12,000 tons of saddlery, 5,500 tons of parts for wire entanglements, 3,200 general service wagons*. Herbert Austin began manufacturing cars at Longbridge in 1905, using a factory which already existed. During the war the government took the works over, extending and adapting them. Here large guns were re-lined, aeroplanes built and huge numbers of shells produced. The factory employed over 12,000 people. Shown as 'Longbridge Works' on the large scale OS map of 1904 it was not shown at all on the 1916 edition. Also invisible was the station used by the workers and their special trains. This consisted of an island platform on the Halesowen branch, next to the Bristol Road. It was open by July 1915, together with extra sidings for the works and a signal box at Longbridge East. Two workers' trains ran daily from New Street and as the number of workers grew and shift patterns developed, the train service was modified. By 1917 there were morning, evening and afternoon trains, via both the West Suburban and Camp Hill lines. By 1918 there were 5 early morning trains into Longbridge and 4 out to take the night shift away. The Great Western ran workers' trains from the Halesowen direction. By 1918 it provided 3 morning trains into Longbridge and 2 out, with the reverse happening in the evenings. A new loop was brought into use in 1917, together with a signal box at Longbridge West. This eased congestion and meant that trains arriving from New Street no longer had to travel

to Rubery as empty stock. Rubery also received hospital trains bearing war wounded. These men were destined for the large hospitals at Hollymoor and Rubery Hill, both within easy reach of the station and both converted for military use. Temporary platforms were also built on the main line at Longbridge, south of the junction with the branch, an alternative to Rubery for some hospital trains. After the war Longbridge Works resurfaced on the maps and it reverted to making cars. The workers' trains continued to run; the hospital trains did not.

With the re-opening of wartime closures, and the restoration of pre-war express schedules, there came other interesting proposals. The government of the day, like many others since, paid lip service to improving the railways, including investigating the benefits of electrification. This generated an article in "Railway Magazine" (May 1919) in which the author remarked, *"One can easily conceive that the network of railways in that area (the Black Country) will in due course be electrically equipped, for goods and mineral as well as passenger traffic, between Wolverhampton, Walsall, Dudley, Birmingham and Coventry. A natural development is to complete equipment southwards to link up with the London & North Western electric lines at Watford, if they have not extended further from London by that time, so that a London-Birmingham-Wolverhampton express passenger service, and electric goods and mineral working for more than 100 miles continuously, come within the range of practical possibilities."* It was to be almost half a century before these thoughts were converted into reality.

Of more immediate concern was the National Railway Strike of 1919, which lasted from September 26th to October 5th. Only a few trains ran during the strike, although numbers gradually increased and, of the three companies serving Birmingham, the Midland was the least affected. The dispute was about wages,

Lapworth looking south, about 1905. The station was named Kingswood from its opening in 1854 until 1902. The Henley-in-Arden branch opened in 1894 and closed with effect from 1st January 1915. Its bay platform and signal can be seen beyond the milk churns and the footbridge. The branch left the main line at Rowington Junction, to the south. The train appears to be an auto train; it could have just left the branch as one of the few through services between Henley and Birmingham. The oil lighting is shown to good effect.

(Lens of Sutton)

which had not kept pace with inflation generated by the war, and about conditions, especially the long hours. The strike was settled by what came to be known as the National Agreement. This laid down a minimum weekly wage for all grades, beginning with £2/11/0 (£2.55) for platform porters. The agreement specified a maximum eight-hour working day before overtime was payable – previously it had been twelve hours. The old custom of each train crew having its 'own' locomotive soon died. It had been reasonable when they were on the footplate for half the day and the engine was either being prepared or disposed of for much of the other half. However, the eight hour day meant that the same loco could often be used for two shifts every day, with different crews, so it could pass through the hands of several crews within a short while.

Although the strike was successful in obtaining the better working conditions which were unquestionably justified, it was a disaster for the railways in another sense. For the first time in such a dispute the government – which at the outset had no idea how long the strike would last or how bitter it might become – ensured that all the big cities were kept well supplied with food and other essentials, such supplies being transported by road and under government supervision. The railways' virtual monopoly of land transport was at an end.

FOCUS ON DUDLEY

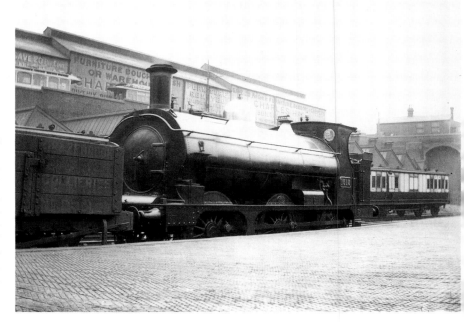

1501 Class 0-6-0 GW saddle tank No.1513 at Dudley c.1903. As well as the LNW carriage, notice the diamond patterned platform surface provided by the Staffordshire blue bricks, a locally owned wagon, two single-deck tramcars and a house with flithy first storey windows. In common with their modern counterparts, the furniture warehouses seem to be offering permanently discounted stock. This picture – one of many fine examples of his art – was taken by Thomas Hinckley, a railwayman based in Walsall at this time.

(Thomas Hinckley; Roger Carpenter collection)

Dudley station about 1910, with a train entering on the Great Western line for Stourbridge, Worcester and Oxford. This joint Great Western/London & North Western station had separate ticket windows, separate goods sheds and – seen here – separate signal boxes, both to the standard designs of their respective companies.

(Lens of Sutton)

This view of Dudley station from the bottom of Castle Hill shows auto trailer No.45, plus 0-6-0 pannier tank, in the bay in the Great Western part of the station, about 1946. The GW calling-on signal is distinguished by the usual white circle on the arm. *(Lens of Sutton)*

One of the many Great Western 0-6-0 pannier tanks, 3745 of the 5700 Class, works a train of empty stock. It has just left the 'Bumble Hole' line (extreme left) to join the Oxford Worcester & Wolverhampton line, 11th June 1962. The train is heading northwards through Blowers Green, a station in a state of terminal distress, just before closure.

(Michael Mensing)

Great Western diesel railcar No.8 waits at Dudley with a service to Stourbridge Junction, about 1947. The windows are exceptionally large, giving good all-round vision, but passenger access was limited to one door on each side of the car. Driver access was via a door at one end only, the far end in this view. Successfully stacking assorted shapes and sizes of parcels onto platform trolleys was a once familiar art form, now lost. The young couple have eyes only for each other. *(Lens of Sutton)*

Urban decay in the days of post-war austerity. A Dudley-Snow Hill Great Western railcar of later, more angular design, leaves Great Bridge, about 1947. This was one of the stations that closed during World War I, re-opening in 1920. The facilities and train service on offer remained poor - as they did at many local stations throughout the West Midlands. They would not survive the forthcoming triple blow of improved bus services, an end to petrol rationing and a huge increase in car ownership. *(Don Powell collection)*

34

CHAPTER THREE : 1920-1929

[Diary : Notes : Along the Lickey Route : Freight]

Diary

1920

January 5th – Birmingham Snow Hill-Dudley service restored and Great Bridge (GW) station re-opened.

1921

First "Claughtons" and G2 "Super Ds" built by LNWR.

July – Birmingham-London trains by both routes accelerated to a post-war best of 2 hours 15 minutes.

October 3rd – Two-hour trains between Birmingham and London restored on both routes.

November 26th – Serious accident at Birmingham New Street, when the 2.10pm Bristol-Sheffield express ran into the rear of the 4.12pm Birmingham-Derby local train.

1923

First "Castle" Class locos built by GWR

January 1st – The 1921 Railways Act came into force, the 'Grouping' of all lines into the 'Big Four' companies – GWR, LMS, LNER and SR. In the West Midlands, Great Western lines remained as they had been, LNWR and Midland lines became part of the London Midland & Scottish Railway (LMS).

July 9th – Coleshill, on the old Whitacre-Hampton line, renamed Maxstoke, six years after closure to passengers; Forge Mills, on the Whitacre-Birmingham line, became Coleshill.

November 4th – New booking hall opened at Walsall station, the famous 'drum' which lasted until 1978.

1924

May 1st – Pleck station re-opened.

1925

January 1st – Sutton Coldfield Town and Church Road stations closed.

GWR summer time-table – New train linking Wolverhampton LL (dep.9.45am) and Snow Hill (10.15) with Brighton (arr.2.15pm), Eastbourne (3.00) and Hastings (3.42). The Birmingham-Brighton journey time of four hours compares with 3 hours 54 minutes and 4 hours 22 minutes by the two trains in the 1997 time-table. This is one cross country route where no real improvements have been made in more than seventy years!

May 11th – Wombourn line opened to passengers.

July 13th – North Walsall station closed.

1926

First "Crab" 2-6-0 freight locos built by LMS

May 4th-12th – General Strike. Rail traffic in the Birmingham area paralysed.

1927

Simplified GWR coach livery introduced this year, plain chocolate and cream without panels.

First "King" Class locos built by GWR. At first some writers described them as "Super Castles".

First "Royal Scot" locos built by LMS.

First of a new class of 2-6-4 tank locos (4P) built by LMS.

Ex-Midland 4-4-0 Compounds now hauling some of the 2 hour Birmingham expresses.

In the LMS winter time-table for 1927-8 the "Pines Express" (Manchester-Birmingham-Bournemouth) also conveyed through carriages between Liverpool Lime St. and Southampton.

December 5th – Public passenger service between Halesowen and Old Hill withdrawn.

1928

First "Hall" Class locos built by GWR.

May 11th – A section of Cofton Tunnel, between Longbridge and Barnt Green, collapsed as it was being prepared for demolition, killing four workmen.

1929

First 5100 Class tank engines and first 5700 Class pannier tank engines built by GWR.

January 26th-28th – Last section of Cofton Tunnel demolished and debris removed.

A "Crab" freight loco No.2892, at Bescot on 4th August 1947.

(F. W. Shuttleworth)

Notes

This was the decade when steam locomotives really entered the modern era, with several notable new types to be seen around the Midlands. The LMS gave us the "Crabs", a large class (245 members) of 2-6-0 freight locos (5F) designed by Fowler in 1926 and so-called because of their link motion. A new heavy 2-6-4 passenger tank, numbered 23xx, emerged in 1927. The Great Western offered two numerous classes of tank engine, the 5100 (2-6-2) and 5700 (0-6-0 pannier tank), both in 1929.

The highest profile, naturally, was given to express passenger locomotives. The first "Castles" were built at Swindon in 1923, a more powerful version of the "Saints" of 1906, making them the most powerful express locos in the country. However, they lost this distinction in 1926, to the new "Lord Nelson" locos of the Southern Railway. This dent to the pride and prestige of 'God's Wonderful Railway' concentrated the thoughts of its general Manager, Sir Felix Pole, who virtually ordered Charles Collett to produce something bigger and better as soon as possible. Thanks to enthusiastic hard work by Collett, staff and workers at Swindon the first of the new class was completed in less than a year. It had slightly smaller driving wheels than the Castles or Saints, a higher boiler pressure of 250lb./sq.in. and more power, with a tractive effort of 40,000lbs., compared to 31,625lbs. for the Castles and 33,500lbs. for the Nelsons. The weight over each main axle was an unprecedented 22 tons, giving it a special 'double red' route restriction. It had been intended to name these 'Super Castles' after cathedrals, but when the first one was to take part in the centenary celebrations of the Baltimore & Ohio Railroad, Sir Felix saw the opportunity to 'fly the flag' for the GWR and Great Britain and asked the king if it could bear his name; thus No.6000 became "King George V". The other 29 also bore the names of English kings, in reverse chronological order. No.6029 "King Stephen" (1135-54) and 6028 "King Henry II" (1154-89) became respectively "King Edward VIII" and "King George VI" in due course. These highly successful locos were used principally on the West of England main line at first, then on the Birmingham line from the 1930s. There was always a number based at Wolverhampton. None was stabled at Tyseley, the shed for the Birmingham-Bristol line, as normal traffic levels over that line did not warrant it and the double red route restriction would not allow it.

The rise of the "Lord Nelsons" had prompted some sleepless nights on the LMS too, and a month after "King George V" took to the rails the first of Fowler's new design, No.6100 "Royal Scot" entered service. They were less powerful than the "Kings" (TE 33,150lbs.) but were soon proving themselves on the Anglo-Scottish expresses. They later became familiar sights on some cross-country workings, such as the "Pines Express", but did not haul the Birmingham-Euston trains on a regular basis until after the Second World War.

The poor positioning of signals combined with driver carelessness to cause a fatal accident on the Midland side of New Street station, on Saturday 26th November 1921. The 4.12pm local to Derby was standing at Platform 4. It was six minutes late and the loco was just being coupled to the carriages. At this moment a Bristol-Sheffield express entered the same platform and passed the signal halfway along it, which was set at danger, supposedly protecting the local. The driver had not seen the signal, thought his fireman told him it was 'off' rather than 'on' and although he made an emergency brake application at the last moment there was a fearful impact, even though the speed had been brought down to less than 10mph.

"The express came into contact with the rear of this train, an empty guard's van receiving the force of the impact and being forced upon the next third-class carriage. The force of the collision lifted the body of the carriage right up to the girders of the footbridge which crosses the station. The girders of the bridge formed a stopblock and undoubtedly saved the other part of the train from being damaged." (Birmingham Post).

The guard's van was not quite empty – Frank Fisher, a parcels foreman who was standing in the middle of it, was thrown back onto some mailbags. He scrambled to the door and got out, shaken but unhurt – "How I escaped is a marvel as I was the nearest person to the spot at which the crash occurred. I did not get a scratch or bruises anywhere." Others were less fortunate. Three people were killed in the third-class carriage – a married father of three from Tamworth, a single bricklayer from Handsworth and a baby girl, the daughter of a couple living in Dudley Road, whose father was serving as a soldier in Ireland. Sixteen other people were injured, fourteen on the local and two on the platform; nobody aboard the express sustained any injury. The Inspecting Officer at the enquiry, Colonel Pringle, criticised the poor siting of the signals, as a result of which they were replaced by tailor-made colour lights in 1924. Looking rather like early traffic lights, they remained in use until the rebuilding of the 1960s.

The 1920s saw the first significant closure of a passenger service in the area. The Halesowen Railway, as has already been described in Chapter Two, played an important part in transporting war workers to the Austin Works at Longbridge, as well as war wounded to the hospitals at Rubery, during the First World War. It had been opened in 1883 between Halesowen and Halesowen Junction (Longbridge), jointly operated by the Great Western and Midland. The section from Halesowen to Old Hill was exclusively Great Western. The largest structure on the line was the viaduct over Dowery Dell, 660 feet long and 100 feet high. At the beginning of the twentieth century there were five trains each way between King's Norton and Halesowen, some of which were mixed (passengers and goods), an economy measure begun in 1892. Between 1901 and 1905 there was much extra freight activity - and welcome extra income for the line – as building materials for both Frankley Reservoir and Hollymoor Hospital were supplied to their sites via a contractor's branch almost a mile long, which connected with the Halesowen Railway at Rubery station.

In 1905 (on July 1st!) the Great Western began a more intensive service between Old Hill and Halesowen, with no fewer than 24 trains each way operated by new rail motors. Coombes Holloway Halt opened at the same time. The service frequency was halved in September, when new halts were opened and a rail motor service began between Old Hill and Dudley. The Old Hill-Halesowen service improved again, with 26 trains each way by the outbreak of war in 1914.

The five daily trains between Halesowen and King's Norton continued until the end of 1916 after which, as a wartime economy, they were reduced – to a daily morning train from Halesowen (through to New St.) and a mid-afternoon return from King's Norton, which ran on Saturdays only. Such a 'service' could not sustain public support. It was not improved at the end of the war and petered out on a date that is now uncertain, probably in May 1919.

During the 1920s the rail motor service between Halesowen and Old Hill was almost as frequent as ever, with 23 trips each way but as local bus services improved, trains on this short line became vulnerable. In 1927 the GWR decided to meet bus competition by replacing the trains with buses of its own, thinking that Halesowen passengers travelling beyond Old Hill would be happy with a road/rail service. Halesowen Urban

There is no doubt that diesel and electric locomotives are cleaner, faster and far more efficient than steam – but when it comes to the sheer display of energy and power, there is no contest! 6026 "King John" is an exhilarating sight as it approaches Lapworth at over 80mph with an express for Paddington on 25th August 1962. The train had originated at Pwllheli, although the King, with its 'double red' route restriction unique to the class, would not have been allowed anywhere near it before Shrewsbury.   *(Robert Darlaston)*

Looking at this picture it is almost possible to hear the roar and feel the vibrations as 136 tons of "King" –No.6008 "King James II" – hurtles through Small Heath & Sparkbrook with the 2.10pm Paddington to Birkenhead express on 7th May 1960.   *(Michael Mensing)*

District Council actually recommended that the proposals be approved, while the Clerk to neighbouring Rowley Regis Council damned them with the faintest of praise, noting merely that, "The most the council would say was that it did not object to the bus service". The trains were replaced by buses on 5th December 1927 and so Halesowen had the dubious distinction of becoming the first town in the Birmingham area to lose its rail passenger service. Almost as a foretaste of the Beeching era in the 1960s, it was only a short while (4th April 1928), before Halesowen UDC was complaining about the unreliability of the bus service and the poor way it connected with the trains at Old Hill.

However, workmen's trains continued along the Halesowen Railway for many years, mainly to serve the Austin car plant at Longbridge. Different sources sometimes give differing closure dates for this service, because it was actually a group of services. Closure of the various sections occurred as follows: Old Hill-Halesowen – 31st March 1928; Old Hill-Longbridge – 29th August 1958; Halesowen-Northfield – 1st January 1960. The line closed completely in January 1964 and Dowery Dell viaduct was dismantled in April 1965. As today's motorists travel towards Birmingham on the Halesowen by-pass, just before the Sandvik factory as the road rises on the approach to the M5, there is no longer any clue that a railway once bridged the road here. Only the stub into what is now the Rover works remains, as busy as ever with freight for the car plant.

A scene taken before the Great Western's Old Hill-Halesowen service was converted to steam railmotor operation in 1905. A train from Halesowen to Old Hill is about to enter the short tunnel under Haden Hill. *(courtesy of Birmingham Post & Mail)*

The narrow spindly structure of Dowery Dell Viaduct, photographed about 1930. *(Don Powell)*

A splendid period piece at Halesowen, probably dating from the very beginning of the twentieth century. The train is entering the station from the Rubery direction, passing under the bridge carrying Mucklow Hill. The platform garden, with foliage skilfully trained around fence posts and cross-members, displays all the symptoms of at least one green-fingered railwayman with plenty of time to spare between trains. *(Lens of Sutton)*

Another view of Halesowen looking towards Mucklow Hill. Behind the GWR auto train, which is facing towards the camera and Old Hill, a Midland train leaves for Rubery and Northfield. The line between Halesowen and Halesowen Junction (at Longbridge) was built and operated jointly by the Great Western and Midland – it is remarkable that either company sanctioned the erection of such a shoddy looking footbridge. *(Lens of Sutton)*

A workmen's service to Halesowen and Old Hill leaves Longbridge on the last day of operation, 29th August 1958, hauled by ex-Great Western 0-6-0 pannier tank No.7448.   *(Robert Darlaston)*

Passenger services along the Wombourn line came and went almost in the twinkling of an eye. The Great Western had wanted to build a line linking Wolverhampton with Bridgnorth, as a Light Railway, in 1899. It would have had a branch, going south near Wombourn and Himley, to join up with an existing line at Kingswinford. A GWR bus service between Wolverhampton and Bridgnorth began in 1904 and the direct railway was never built. The branch however, was built, in modified form. Construction began in 1913 and by the outbreak of war most of the earthworks and some of the stations were nearing completion. Soon work was reduced to a trickle until, after the completion of the last bridge over the long cutting at Castlecroft in 1916, a handful of men were left to guard and maintain what little plant had not already been removed.

Working conditions for this very late railway were much as they had been in the nineteenth century. The contractor set up camp at Wombourn and hundreds of men and boys worked on the line. Many had come from afar, those who were local had left poorly paid farm work, causing the farmers to be short-handed. The contractor, Perry & Co. of Bow, East London, used numerous horses, nine standard gauge locos and three steam shovels during construction. Local boys leaving school in 1914, aged 14, or even 13, could expect an initial wage of 14 shillings (70p) for a 56 hour week if they opted to work on building the railway!

Perry & Co. were deemed to have completed their contract in 1920, leaving the GWR to complete the railway itself. Other more important works and routine maintenance had been interrupted by the war, and completion of the Wombourn line, still officially known as the Wolverhampton & Bridgnorth Railway, was low on their list of priorities. No attempt was made to exploit further the coal seams in the area, at Baggeridge, the main reason for promotion of the branch in the first place. Eventually the line was opened, to goods traffic, on 11th January 1925 and to passengers on 11th May. It was single track, with a passing loop at Wombourn and some provision for the track to be doubled; Tettenhall and Himley, for example, each had a second platform which was destined never to be used. The service was operated by rail motors, with eight trains each way between Wolverhampton, Wombourn and Stourbridge Junction, where they shared a platform with the Stourbridge Town train. There was also a morning extra between Wombourn and Wolverhampton. It soon became obvious that few people felt the need for this railway. It served nowhere of importance and was an indirect duplication of a line that already existed. By 1925 bus services were developing and a few people already had access to a car – its cause was hopeless. The train service was reduced to five in each direction, but when passenger receipts for 1931 were just £741 (ie; 4 shillings and 8 pence [23p] per train!) the GWR decided to reduce the number of trains further – to nil. The last train ran, with no ceremony and little lament, on 29th October 1932.

40

A family scene at Compton Halt, on the Wombourn line, August 1926. The posters advertise the delights of Devon and Cornwall, but this trip was nearer to home. Members of the Johnson and Cox families wait for the rail motor to Wombourn, for a walk on the hills.

(courtesy of Wolverhampton Archives & Local Studies and Cecil Cox)

Train crew and station staff pose with auto train No.5 at Himley, shortly after the service started. The number of staff, the full facilities at the station and even the generous length of the platform have all come much too late to this rural location. The trains were few and the line followed no natural route between communities : this service was stillborn.

(Lens of Sutton)

So what of those lads who had sweated to build the line for just 70p a week; wasn't their hard work all rather pointless? Not exactly. The Wombourn line was a very useful freight route, relieving pressure on others in the area and providing another alternative around the congested Birmingham and Black Country lines, particularly during the Second World War. The junction with the Wolverhampton-Shrewsbury line, at Oxley, faced both ways, so trains leaving the branch could head north without reversal. The branch itself continued to generate freight from Courtauld's, near Oxley, and Baggeridge Colliery, with its sidings at Gornal. Trains conveying carpets from Kidderminster, cars from the Morris factory at Oxford and fruit from the Vale of Evesham all used the line on a regular basis.

Tettenhall and Wombourn stations came alive again in the summer of 1944 as some of those wounded on D-Day and its aftermath were transferred from ambulance trains and taken to the Royal and New Cross hospitals in Wolverhampton. About forty such trains ran that summer. General goods traffic continued throughout the 1950s, but the last train ran on 27th February 1965. For just over forty years the Wombourn line had been a useful freight route in peace and war – the men and boys who built it had not laboured in vain.

WOLVERHAMPTON and STOURBRIDGE JUNCTION—(Rail Motor Cars—One class only).

Week Days only.

Miles	Low Level Station.	mrn	mrn	mrn		aft		aft	X	aft	aft			E Except Saturdays. U Change at Brettell Lane. X Runs 7 minutes later on Sats. ¶ "Halts at Compton and at Penn between Tettenhall and Wombourn; and at Gornal, at Pensnett, at Bromley, and at Brockmoor between Himley and Brettell Lane.
	Wolverhampton ...dep.	8 0	9 15	1145	....	1250		1250	2 30	6 10	9 0	....		
1	Dunstall Park	8 3	9 18	1148	....	1253		1253	2 33	6 13	9 3	....		
3½	Tettenhall ¶	8 10	9 25	1155	....	1 0		1 0	2 40	6 20	9 10	....		
7½	Wombourn	8 22	9 38	12 7	....	1 12		1 15	2 54	6 35	9 25	....		
9½	Himley ¶		9 43		....			1 20	2 59	6 40	9 30	....		
14	Brettell Lane [118, 133]		10 0		....			1 37	3 16	6 57	9 47	....		
16	Stourbridge Jun.84,arr.		10 6		....			2 0	3 22	7 24	9 53	....		

STOURBRIDGE JUNCTION and WOLVERHAMPTON—(Rail Motor Cars—One class only).

Week Days only.

Miles		mrn	mrn	mrn		aft		aft	aft	aft		U Change at Brettell Lane. ¶ "Halts" at Brockmoor, at Bromley, at Pensnett, and at Gornal, between Brettell Lane and Himley; at Penn, and at Compton, between Wombourn and Tettenhall.
	Stourbridge Junction ...dep.	6 50	..	1020	....			1130	4 38	7 40	....	
2	Brettell Lane ¶	6 55	..	1026	....			1 42	4 47	7 46	....	
6½	Himley	7 12	..	1042	....			1 58	5 0	8 2	....	
8½	Wombourn ¶	7 20	8 25	1048	....	1210	1 55	2 55	6 8	9 ..	....	
12½	Tettenhall	7 33	8 38	11 1	....	1223	2 8	2 18	5 19	8 22	....	
15	Dunstall Park [108, 474]	7 41	8 47	11 9	....	1231	2 16	2 26	5 27	8 30	....	
16	Wolverhampton (L.L.)..arr.	7 46	8 50	1112	....	1234	2 19	2 31	5 30	8 33	....	

✱✱ For OTHER TRAINS between Stourbridge Junction and Wolverhampton, see page 116.

Bradshaw's Railway Guide for October 1929, and the Wombourn line has already lost half the trains it had on opening in 1925.

(courtesy of Robert Pearson)

Along the Lickey Route

The Lickey Incline is at its most impressive when approached from the south, but instead of describing it in isolation, I prefer to place it in the context of its route, the main line linking Bristol with Birmingham. This creates a problem, as the last main line station of any consequence before the Lickey, for a northbound train, is Cheltenham, far outside the scope of this book.

I shall begin, instead, with a glance at Worcester Shrub Hill, situated on a loop off the main line. Today, Worcester's two stations – the other is at Foregate Street in the city centre – share a healthy half-hourly local service to Birmingham via Stourbridge and a less frequent semi-fast service via Bromsgrove. Shrub Hill is sometimes thought of as purely Great Western territory, where ex-GW signal boxes and lower quadrant semaphore signals still rule. In fact it was a joint station, shared with the Midland Railway, which had running rights over the loop line and indeed over the Worcester-Hereford line too. The Midland main line, opened in 1840, by-passed Worcester. The first railway to serve Worcester, which established its headquarters at Shrub Hill, was the Oxford Worcester & Wolverhampton (OWW), later to form part of the Great Western. The first part of the OWW to be completed, in 1850, was a short section from the Midland main line to Shrub Hill. It formed the

southern bit of the loop. At first the Midland operated it as its own branch, the OWW having a line, but as yet no locos or stock to run on it! In February 1852 the remainder of the Worcester loop was opened (the OWW line as far as Stourbridge followed three months later) and the Midland began diverting some of its expresses along it. In this way Worcester was served by selected Bristol-Birmingham trains until as recently as 1982, when InterCity services abandoned the loop.

Droitwich is on the loop, five miles north of Worcester, where the routes to Birmingham divide. There has been a settlement here since Roman times, thanks to the occurrence of salt and brine. The trade in salt grew when a canal link with the Severn was constructed near the end of the eighteenth century. It prospered further with the arrival of the railway, which brought visitors to the town seeking relief from rheumatism and arthritis at the brine baths. Many were not able bodied, so when the station was rebuilt in 1899 the GWR took their needs into account, making each platform accessible via a gently sloping roadway as an alternative to the footbridge.

Droitwich's salt king, John Corbett, gave some of his land adjacent to the Worcester platform, to provide an access road and turning circle for carriages and horse cabs plying between the station, baths and hotels. He also donated £700 for new platform

The joint Great Western-Midland station at Worcester Shrub Hill. The trains in view are Great Western but the livery is definitely not chocolate and cream. An overall brown was introduced in 1909, quickly replaced by crimson lake in 1912. The two original Oxford Worcester & Wolverhampton engine sheds lie in the distance. A train is just entering the station from the Hereford line, hauled by 0-6-0 No.427, and another is leaving for that line from the through loop. 0-4-2 tank No.835 waits in the bay, probably with a train for Bromyard and Leominster. The distant signals are still painted red and the locos are very nineteenth century, their splendid polished domes being a hallmark of Churchward's predecessor, William Dean. *(courtesy of Birmingham Central Library)*

buildings. He lived on the edge of Droitwich at Chateau Impney, built to remind his pretty young French wife of home (alas, she left him for another man). After he died in 1901, two statues from the grounds – busts of a Roman god and goddess – were placed in the terraced gardens on the station's Birmingham platform. The god was decapitated by vandals in 1996. The former bookstall on the Worcester platform, now a disused store, pre-dates the 1899 buildings, which were replaced in the 1980s. The 1907 signal box has a 79 lever frame. It stands in the junction north of the station, the frame facing the Stourbridge line. All its semaphore signals are of the lower quadrant type, with two on the Birmingham platform having a central pivot.

Some visitors to the brine baths had a successful stay in the town, arriving in bath chairs or on stretchers, yet departing on crutches. Others who had arrived with just crutches or sticks felt able to abandon them before catching the train home. The crutches were stored at the station for a period – unusual items of long term left luggage – in case their owners ever needed them again. Despite the popularity of the baths, the station at Droitwich was not re-named 'Droitwich Spa' until 1923.

There was originally a northern spur at Droitwich (see main map). When the line towards Stoke Works was being constructed during 1849, Roman remains were found in Bays Meadow and along the course of the spur. "Antiquities & Folklore of Worcestershire" by the splendidly named Jabez Allies, records the discovery of foundations, a mosaic pavement, pottery and coins. Parts of the pavement were removed to Worcester Museum. The only portion of the site examined was that which

had been exposed in the making of the railway, no record was kept of the precise location of the finds, and no attempt was made to excavate further. Later, when preparing the site within the railway triangle for new factories in 1947, more building material and pottery came to light. The northern spur in its turn has now become an antiquity. There is no evidence that it was ever used to any extent. There were never any time-tabled passenger trains over it. The link to the Stourbridge line was severed in 1890 and it was converted into sidings, which lasted until the early twentieth century.

Old OS maps also indicate a branch to the Covercroft Salt Works from just north of the station, leaving the goods sidings by a steeply climbing curve, more severe than the Lickey at 1:34. It passed north of the workhouse before turning south to the salt works, which had its own loco, built by Manning Wardle of Leeds in 1878.

The most important salt works during the twentieth century was outside Droitwich, at Stoke Works. The wayside station was near the northern end of the Worcester loop, at the boundary between the Great Western and Midland/LMS. From here the main line leads towards the rising ground in the distance, at the foot of which is the start of the most famous railway incline in Britain.

The main line of the Birmingham & Gloucester Railway - a company which amalgamated with others to form the Midland in 1844 – opened in 1840. Its promoters wanted a route that was cheap to construct and direct. Near Bromsgrove, confronted with rising ground, the line is so direct that, instead of finding an

The Droitwich Triangle, seen from the grounds of Dodderhill Church. After the north curve ceased to be used as a through line in 1890, part of it became sidings until the early 1900s. Today the formation is occupied by factory units. There is still a footpath across the line, with a gatepost made from broad gauge rail. Bays Meadow Cottage, on the right, derelict since the 1950s, was demolished in 1997.

(Frank Brown collection)

easier but slightly longer way through the contours (there is at least one alternative, a little to the west) it simply mounts the landscape head on. This results in an incline rising at 1:37.7 for a little over two miles (some sources quote 2 miles 4 chains, others increase it to 10 chains). The foot of the incline, at Bromsgrove station, is 256 feet above sea level, the summit at Blackwell is 300 feet higher. The climb begins in a shallow cutting, which gives way to an embankment, ever increasing in height before the short deep cutting near the summit. Virtually all trains required assistance when ascending and extreme caution when descending. Bromsgrove was the headquarters of the Birmingham & Gloucester company, with an engine shed alongside the station whose prime purpose was to provide assisting engines (I have avoided the word 'banking' as, in early years, most trains were assisted from in front by a pilot loco because buffer heights had not been standardised). From the 1860s these had the 0-6-0 wheel arrangement. As train lengths and weights increased around the turn of the century such locos often worked in pairs, or even threes, creating huge plumes of smoke at the rear of a Bristol-Derby express and causing a wave of sound that could be heard two miles away. Such working certainly looked impressive, but it was hopelessly uneconomic,

involving two or three banking locos, each with its fuel and footplate crew, plus other such engines on standby twenty-four hours per day. Something bigger was needed; bigger meant better, more efficient and more cost effective, a 'Super Banker'.

By 1910 such a loco had arrived on Derby's drawing board, in three different guises. There was a large tank engine with 10 driving wheels, an even larger one with 12 driving wheels coupled in two sets of 6 (a 0-6-6-0 wheel arrangement) and an articulated tank engine (2-6-6-2) over 59 feet (18 metres) long, weighing 120 tonnes. This confusion of big ideas generated a special committee of Midland Railway Board members, which met in 1912 to discuss details of planning and construction. Henry Fowler's design for the loco, already unofficially christened 'Big Emma', was completed by May 1914, but construction was delayed by the onset of war.

That war saw more traffic than ever before over the Lickey, with heavy freight, troop and hospital trains. The need for the super banker was greater than ever, but the need for Derby works to build tanks, gun carriages and other instruments of death was even greater, so Big Emma had to wait. Construction began in 1919 and the loco was completed in December. Some of the men in the workshops had recently returned from active service in

27th July 1911. The train has just passed Blackwell distant signal on its way up the Lickey. High summer; not only was 1911 one of the hottest and sunniest summers of the century, but this picture also represents the high summer of Midland Railway locomotive and carriage design. A Johnson 'spinner', No.630, with its great 7ft.4in. driving wheels, pilots 2-4-0 No.197, a Johnson rebuild of a Kirtley loco. The banking loco is virtually invisible from this angle. The rake of eight David Bain carriages is led by a twelve-wheeled dining car. The whole ensemble is an example of the comfort and quality routinely provided by the Midland, a luxury train for ordinary people.

(National Railway Museum)

France, where they had known of the three colossal rail-mounted super guns, each called Big Bertha and all used by the Germans for bombarding Paris. Emma became Bertha, and so the Lickey banker was named after the wife of Gustav Krupp, head of Germany's main armaments dynasty.

2290, as Bertha was officially known, was a 0-10-0, a decapod. The 4'7" driving wheels were all braked, the cylinders were inclined at 1 in 7 and the working boiler pressure was 180lbs/sq.in. The electric headlamp, necessary for banking at night or in fog, was an afterthought, not fitted until 1921, after brief conversion to oil burning following severe coal shortages, the result of a national miners' strike. The headlamp was powered by its own generator and could be swivelled up, down and sideways. Sometimes it was known to highlight the antics of courting couples in cars parked in Pikes Pool Lane, alongside the incline.

On completion this was the largest loco on the Midland and the most powerful in Britain, with a tractive effort of 43,313 lb. (ie; 19.34 tons - the tractive effort is the force exerted on the drawbar of a loco when pulling a load, although 'push' applies in this case). The all-round cab gave full protection for the crew whatever the direction of travel. Big Bertha had a total weight of 105.25 tons, including the 31.5 ton tender, which had a small size and capacity relative to its loco, only 13 tons of coal and 2050 gallons of water. This avoided unnecessary weight, as Bertha was hardly likely to stray far and there was always a plentiful supply of fuel at Bromsgrove. 2290 was a successful and

efficient banking engine from 1920 until withdrawal in 1956, by which time it had travelled 836,400 miles, the vast majority of them on the Lickey. In view of the increasing volume of traffic over the incline it is surprising that no other similar locos were built to share the work. Others were tried, notably an 0-8-4 tank version of the ex-LNWR 'Super D' in 1929, and Gresley's unique 1925-built 2-8-8-2 monster Garratt No.69999 twenty years later. Neither was a success on the Lickey.

In 1924 Fowler designed a class of 0-6-0 tank engines, classified 3F, with a tractive effort of 20,834 pounds. Over 400 of these powerful little tugs were built, for use on freight, banking and shunting duties over much of the LMS. From then until the 1950s, as Big Bertha was destined to remain an only child, she was almost invariably accompanied at Bromsgrove by a gaggle of these 'Jinties', up to eight being in steam and ready for duty at the busiest periods.

Charles Lake, writing in "Railway Magazine" in April 1920 gave an interesting glimpse of the incline shortly after Bertha's arrival:-

There are 23 passenger and 30 goods and mineral trains booked to ascend the Incline daily, 7 or 8 minutes being occupied by each passenger train, and 15 minutes by each freight train in running, in addition to which the section is occupied by the stoppage of the trains at Bromsgrove for the bank engine or engines, and again at Blackwell by the bank engines leaving the grade . . . Some of the trains are banked by two 0-6-0 side-tank engines, and others by three of these engines working together, the new locomotive, No.2290, working turn and turn about with them. This engine made about eight return trips in two hours and of course its water and coal supplies have to be replenished frequently."

Virtually no trains worked up the incline unassisted, not surprising when the stock of the lightest passenger trains weighed about 150tons and the maximum number of wagons that even the most powerful freight loco was allowed to haul without a banker was only eight. Before 1914 bankers had always buffered-up at Bromsgrove station, at the foot of the incline, the worst possible place for a standing start, even in ideal weather conditions. From February of that year all trains not calling at the station had the banker(s) come on near the signal box at Bromsgrove South, as they came out of their holding sidings, where the grade was only 1:185. [Bankers were never coupled to the main train, the driver of which, on passing Stoke Works box, had given one, two or three short blasts on his whistle, depending on how many Jinties he thought he needed, assuming Bertha was already busy. The signaller at Stoke Works passed this information to Bromsgrove South.] At the summit the bankers would cease their roar and come to a stand as the main train accelerated away, after which they crossed over to the down line and coasted gently back to Bromsgrove.

By 1930 there were four tracks all the way from New Street to Barnt Green (two double tracks north of King's Norton), with plans to quadruple the line between Bromsgrove South and Stoke Works Junction. This left just the Lickey as double track. With about 150 trains passing through every day – this figure excludes banking engines returning to Bromsgrove – the incline had the potential to develop into a serious bottleneck. The newly quadrupled line between Halesowen Junction (Longbridge) and Barnt Green was re-signalled, as was the incline itself. The Lickey had always been worked under special arrangements and the new signalling emphasised this. There were three main objectives – to operate the incline in safety, to avoid delays and to ensure that no train climbing the bank ever had to stop whilst doing so. A new signal box at Blackwell came into use on 27th April 1930. It had a 55 lever frame which was, unusually, at the back of the box, whereas in most boxes the signalman looked over the frame for a view of the track outside. (Selly Oak, Bournville and Barnt Green Main Line also had their frames at the back.) Blackwell was equipped with track circuits and special signals. Essentially, two trains were allowed to ascend the incline at any one time, both within Blackwell's section, because of the 'Lickey Signal' which, in effect, split the section into two. Leaving Bromsgrove past the station box starter signal, the first Blackwell controlled signal was a new two aspect colour light, the repeater of the special 'Lickey Signal', also two aspect, which followed. There followed a change in track circuit, for Blackwell's distant (colour light), after which came the outer home, which had a distant arm for the next signal, at Blackwell station, and a calling-on arm underneath. The inner home, at the station, also had a calling-on arm. Trains could continue to the next signal, thanks to this arm, even if the section beyond it was still occupied. This saw them over the worst of the gradient without stopping. It minimised the risk of 'bunching' of trains coming up behind. North of Blackwell station, between the two running lines, was a short siding for banking engines, installed in 1930. Beyond was the starting signal, with a distant arm for the 'Linthurst' signal. This Linthurst signal had distant arms worked by Barnt Green Main Line box. A hefty pull at 1,030 yards from that box, they were replaced by colour lights about 1940.

The unique train describer in Blackwell box showed the progress of each train up the bank. There was a repeater describer in Bromsgrove Station box and the signalman there

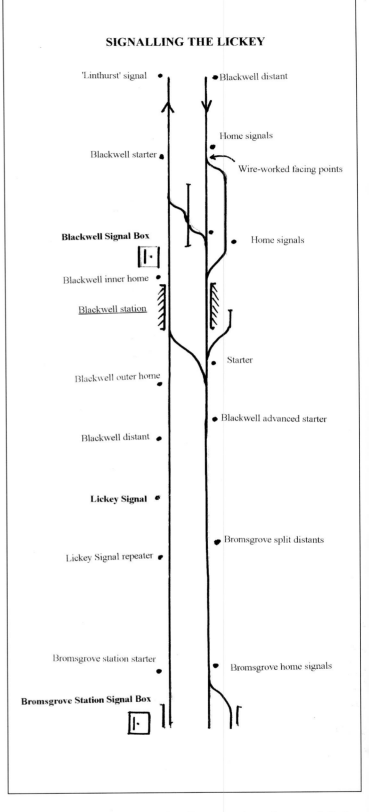

SIGNALLING THE LICKEY

'Linthurst' signal
Blackwell distant
Home signals
Blackwell starter
Wire-worked facing points
Blackwell Signal Box
Home signals
Blackwell inner home
Blackwell station
Starter
Blackwell outer home
Blackwell advanced starter
Blackwell distant
Lickey Signal
Lickey Signal repeater
Bromsgrove split distants
Bromsgrove station starter
Bromsgrove home signals
Bromsgrove Station Signal Box

could offer a train to Blackwell even when the panel lights showed there was already a 'leading train in section' and a 'following train in section'. As soon as the leading train reached the summit and passed out of the section its lights would go out, only to come on again when the 'following train' became the 'leading train' and there was room for the next train to start its assault on the Lickey.

The railway photographer H. C. Casserley was in the right place – Derby – at the right time – New Year's Day 1920 – to witness a trial run by the unique 0-10-0 No.2290, the Lickey Banker. *(H.C.Casserley; Don Powell collection)*

Ascending the Lickey was only half the story; the descent had its own set of problems. Most freight trains were still without a continuous braking system, so they were required to stop before the descent and have the handbrake of at least every third wagon pinned down by the brakesman, who was based at Blackwell. The brakes were released again at Bromsgrove. The maximum permitted speed of freight trains down the incline and through Bromsgrove station was 10mph. The constant friction on the brake blocks during the descent caused the ballast at either side of the down line to be covered with rusty metal dust, giving it a reddish appearance.

There was a crossover at the south end of Blackwell station for the use of returning bankers. A little to the north was a long loop, in which a southbound freight could be held while a passenger train overtook it. When resignalling took place in 1930 the loop points nearer the box were worked by conventional rodding. The facing points, which had to be locked, were too far away for rodding, so they were wire-worked. The wire was of a heavier duty than signal wire, with no means of altering the tension. The two levers controlling these facing points were mounted into a German-type barrel frame and they needed to be turned through 180 degrees! Before the point lever itself could be worked, the other one – the locking lever – had to be pulled to release the point lock. Then the point lever was operated, after which the locking lever was worked a second time to lock the points into

their new position! The hazard of working these levers, with heavy wire and through 180 degrees, was very real, and at least one Blackwell signalman suffered a hernia as a result. Men sometimes refused to work them, putting the loop out of service. They were replaced by motor worked points in the 1950s.

There were home signals at the north and south ends of the loop and, just south of Blackwell station platform, a short siding which could hold about four wagons. This was useful if a train from Birmingham had had a pilot engine, which could be detached, drawn forward and held in the siding. A starter signal protected the crossover, and a southbound train could be held there while the bankers crossed over in front of it. There was an advanced starter a short distance ahead. This had a calling-on signal beneath the main arm. If it was set at danger the home signal at Bromsgrove station had not yet cleared; if it was in the 'off' position, the line was clear through the station. Further down the bank was the split distant for the station, followed by the home signals for the through line and the down platform line.

Today, the situation at the Lickey has changed out of all recognition. Big Bertha has long since departed and the High Speed Trains are hardly slowed in their race to the summit, where there is nothing to show that Blackwell station ever existed. Banking duties for freight are now rare, performed by Bescot locos, strictly 'by prior appointment!'

The German barrel frame signal levers at Barrow Hill box. Two levers of this type were to be found in Blackwell box after 1930. Some levers, to the right, have been pulled 'off' through 180 degrees. All such levers were labelled on both sides. The immense effort required to work them can easily be imagined!

(Don Powell collection)

The unique train describer inside Blackwell Signal Box.

(Don Powell collection)

UP THE LICKEY . . .

A Bristol to York express nears the top of the Lickey Incline, 30th April 1920, hauled by a 4-4-0 Compound and banked by Big Bertha, then brand new. The rake of ten clerestory carriages bears all the hallmarks of David Bain, who succeeded James Clayton as the Midland's carriage & Wagon Superintendent in 1902. His passenger rolling stock had at least as much style and quality as that of his distinguished predecessor.

(National Railway Museum)

One last push! Big Bertha nears the summit of the Lickey at Blackwell, c.1920. The crossover for banking engines is visible, as are the two closely spaced signals. A freight train could be held at the further one when the crossover was in use.   *(Don Powell collection)*

One of Fowler's 4F 0-6-0s of 1911 design, No. 3840, comes over the top and into Blackwell, 12th July 1939.   *(Don Powell collection)*

Even a modest train of just five corridor coaches required the assistance of a 'Jinty'   0-6-0 tank engine for the climb up the Lickey Incline, just north of Pikes Pool Lane, around 1930.
(Don Powell)

AND DOWN AGAIN.

Over four hundred 'Jinty' tanks were built by the LMS, to a Fowler design, from 1924. A handful of them were always to be found clustered at the foot of the Lickey, in readiness for banking duties. Here 7443 and 7425 are about to 'drop off' their train at Blackwell, before crossing over and drifting down the bank, ready to do it all over again. 12th July 1939.
(Don Powell collection)

4-4-0 No.505 starts to descend the Lickey with a Liverpool-Bournemouth express, about 1920. These locos were designed by Johnson in 1884 and rebuilt, with superheater, by Fowler between 1912 and 1923. *(Don Powell collection)*

Having crept down Lickey Bank, 4-4-0 No.511 eases through Bromsgrove station with an excursion for Bournemouth during the spring of 1922. Those with an interest in carriage design will be well rewarded should they examine this photograph through a magnifying glass. *(Don Powell collection)*

A double-headed Bristol express has just descended the Lickey Incline and is seen passing the coaling stage, where a 'Jinty' waits. Both locos appear to be ex-Midland Railway 2P 4-4-0s. Quadrupling of the line south to Stoke Works had just been completed (1933), hence the clean ballast.

(Don Powell)

The next station towards Birmingham is Barnt Green, opened in 1840. It has been the junction for the Redditch branch since 1859. The Midland Railway footbridge here, once again painted in Midland 'red' following the suggestion of a local resident, is a right of way. Well before 1900 Birmingham people had discovered the Lickey Hills as a place for a day out, using the train to Barnt Green to reach them. After 1924, with the extension of the Bristol Road tram route to Rednal, the trains were less busy, although at weekends and bank holidays a train of six non-corridor coaches could still be full and standing. In 1868 the Redditch branch became a through line, known to railwaymen as the 'Gloucester Loop'. Mostly single track, it went via Alcester and Evesham to rejoin the Birmingham-(Gloucester)-Bristol main line at Ashchurch. In this form it generated traffic of its own, especially fruit and vegetables from the Vale of Evesham, not to mention steam rollers and jam from the wayside station and goods yard at Salford Priors. It was also useful as an alternative to the Lickey, especially when the incline was closed for engineering work, or as the result of an accident. On 14th December 1926, for example, the two bankers at the rear of a lunchtime freight train appear to have been over-enthusiastic,

pushing too hard and causing three wagons to rear up and derail near the foot of the incline. The manager of the Bromsgrove station bookstall and an off-duty driver had their chat rudely interrupted by the noise. The accident was close enough for them to run the length of the platform and shout a warning to the crew of the rear banker, who immediately shut off steam and gave a warning blast on the whistle, preventing further damage. The Gloucester Loop was severed as a through route with the closure of the Alcester-Evesham section in 1962, so Redditch sits at the end of a branch once more, as the terminus of the electrified Cross City line.

The biggest single obstacle to quadrupling the main line lay between Barnt Green and Longbridge. This was Cofton Tunnel, a quarter of a mile (400 metres) long and with a bore so narrow that the space between the two tracks was only 5feet 1inch (1.55m), as opposed to the normal 6 feet (1.84m). The tunnel was to be opened out and replaced by a seventy foot deep cutting, concrete lined and containing four tracks. This was an enormous task, employing up to four hundred men from the beginning of 1926 until completion in May 1930. The photograph of demolition in progress (page 54) reveals little mechanisation; this

Barnt Green, about 1910. The train is heading for Blackwell and the top of the Lickey Incline. The standard Midland Railway signals are on tall wooden posts; that on the main line beyond the train has a repeater arm low down. One company touch is the black disc, rather than a vertical bar, on the rear of each signal arm.

(Lens of Sutton)

War is only weeks away, 12th July 1939. Fowler 2-6-2 tank No.16 brings a Redditch - New Street local into Barnt Green. The enamel advertisements for Stephen's Ink (ivory) and Virol (dark orange) were commonplace. They were manufactured by the Selly Oak Enamelling Co., which was served by a private siding south of Selly Oak station. The platform fencing was of the standard Midland Railway pattern.

(Don Powell collection)

The demolition of Cofton Tunnel in progress, April 1928. The remains of the walls, including a refuge, can be seen. A section of remaining roof is also visible. The new concrete wall of the cutting looms above it all. *(Don Powell collection)*

was very much a labour intensive activity. The steam cranes of the contractor, Logan & Hemingway of Doncaster, are on temporary track. The rubble-filled ditch is the trackbed, and the remains of the tunnel wall can be seen, including a platelayers' refuge. The concrete lining of what will be the cutting rears up on the right, while in the distance part of the old tunnel roof has yet to be removed. When the work was still its the early stages, on 11th May 1928, preparations were being made for demolition of the first part of the tunnel roof. It collapsed without warning, killing four workmen. The last section of tunnel was removed in January 1929. By then the cutting was wide enough to take the four tracks, but it was still too shallow in part. A shelf of exceptionally hard rock – 25 feet wide, 12 feet thick and half a mile long – had to be removed before the new tracks could be placed alongside the old, and this took a further fifteen months.

A section of line just over a mile long, from Halesowen Junction to the south end of King's Norton station, had been quadrupled as long ago as 1892. North of King's Norton there were two routes to New Street, so the station became a bottleneck as traffic grew in the early twentieth century. The line through the station was increased to four tracks during 1925. The station itself was completely rebuilt (although the 1849 buildings still survive on the Redditch platform), with two side platforms and an island. Station Road had been on a level crossing at the south end of the platforms. Increased rail traffic, plus the much greater width of the trackbed, meant that this was no longer an option. The road itself was of only minor local importance, with plenty of alternatives, so an expensive road bridge was not thought necessary. The level crossing was removed and replaced by a footbridge, cutting Station Road in two.

The northern end of the Lickey Route splits at King's Norton.

Most passenger trains now take the western route, the Birmingham West Suburban Line, opened as a single track branch to a Birmingham terminus at Granville St. in 1876, widened to two tracks and extended via five tunnels into an enlarged New Street in 1885. There are two mileposts on the platforms at King's Norton, giving two distances to the Midland Railway's headquarters at Derby. The one on the island platform indicates the original main line of 1840, known as the Camp Hill Line, named after what was the last station before Birmingham. All stations on that line closed in 1941. Today, traffic congestion on the roughly parallel Alcester Road (A435) is chronic. There must be many city workers living near it, particularly in Moseley and King's Heath, for whom a revived local rail service would be a most welcome return from the dead.

Freight

At a time when railways had a virtual monopoly of freight traffic, photographs of goods yards are comparatively rare. They were perceived as ordinary, everyday and largely uninteresting – they had been in existence for many years and it seemed likely that they would continue well beyond the foreseeable future.

There are large freight yards today, such as Bescot, Lawley Street and Hams Hall, but in former years there were many more of them, large and small. Before the advent of efficient and computerised sorting of trains, large areas were given over to sorting sidings, where incoming trains were broken up and remarshalled. One such was at Stechford, with 10 long sidings, another was Bushbury, with 9. Large scale maps of the first half of the twentieth century show how many yards there were and just how much space they occupied. The Central Goods station of the Midland Railway stood on more than 10 acres of prime land in the

Brighton Road station, between Moseley and Camp Hill, opened in 1875, as the Birmingham suburbs spread outwards. The station served Balsall Heath, an area of densely packed insanitary slums with chronic health problems and few amenities. This picture shows a train bound for New Street, about 1912. The 0-4-4 tank loco No.1324, for light passenger duties (later classified only as 1P) was to an 1881 design by Samuel Johnson. The first three carriages are six-wheelers, followed by a clerestory, all to designs by James Clayton, the renowned Carriage & Wagon Superintendent of the Midland Railway between 1873 and 1902. Brighton Road signal box closed in 1939, two years ahead of the station.

(Don Powell collection)

heart of Birmingham, a little to the west of New Street station and adjacent to earlier goods facilities, the extensive canal wharfs.

The main LNWR goods station was at Curzon Street, the former passenger terminus of the London & Birmingham Railway. On the eve of the first World War 2,000 men and 600 horses were employed there. It was open 24 hours per day, except Sundays. There were 54 cranes in the yard, including what was then a super-crane with a lift of 20 tons. Some longer distance deliveries and collections were made by a fleet of 10 motor lorries (capacity 2.5 tons, speed 12mph) and one steam lorry (5mph), which had been supplied in 1910. Curzon St. also had stores for beer and wine, a storeroom exclusively for onions, one for newsprint and another, with an early form of temperature and humidity control, for the fashion accessory in the houses of the rich and not too poor – brass bedsteads. A recently enlarged store housed quantities of metal of many types from across the world, awaiting despatch by rail to the foundries of the West Midlands, to be melted down and re-used. The writer of a "Railway Magazine" article (January 1914) was told that at the time of his visit the metal in store was worth about a quarter of a million pounds.

To the north, the goods station at Windsor Street, Aston, received general goods, plus large quantities of house coal and gas coal, the latter for use in the city's main gasworks, which occupied part of the site.

The largest marshalling yard was at Bescot, near Walsall. There were 52 sorting sidings here and wagons were sorted via three humps in the yard. The LNWR Birmingham Control Office was established at Bescot in December 1912 and described in the company's in-house magazine, the "L&NW Railway Gazette" for July 1913. There were three controllers per eight hour shift – Head, Assistant Traffic and Assistant Locomotive Controller – nine men in all. They sat facing a twenty foot long diagram of the lines into which were set small brass sockets *"opposite each signal box, and on the running lines and sidings where it is known goods trains or light engines can stand"*. The controllers were in constant communication with signalmen by phone, who advised them of train movements. They inserted brass pegs into the sockets to correspond with the position of every train. By advising and directing signalmen they had a measure of control over the system, if not over the actual signals. It was hardly a modern power box but the principle was the same.

Like Birmingham, Wolverhampton had goods yards belonging to all three railways in the area. The posed photograph (page 56) of the town's LNWR goods yard, c.1908, shows the railway art of capstan shunting, a feature of many large and cramped yards until the 1960s. Wagons to be transferred from one siding to another were turned on small wooden tables and moved along the cross line, to be turned again by capstan onto the correct siding. Capstans were sited near each table. Larger capstans were

The LNWR Goods Yard at Wolverhampton, 1908.

(courtesy of Wolverhampton Archives & Local Studies)

Bescot Train Control, photographed when new. The track diagram includes Bescot itself, near the centre, and Birmingham New Street, bottom, above the gap between the desks.

(W. E. Hall)

A publicity shot, dating from 1929, of Powell's Timber Yard, Cope Street, Birmingham. The photographer was standing with his back to the island platform of Monument Lane station. The tracks to the left lead into the carriage shed. *(Don Powell collection)*

electrically powered, the smaller ones were free-moving. As can be seen, the rope connects the wagon's axle guard with a powered capstan, via a free one. When the capstanman operates the foot treadle (unseen, but near his foot), the capstan rotates, drawing the wagon onto the table. The table can now be unlocked; the lock is visible beneath the rope. Further operation of the capstan will turn the wagon through 90°, ready for running on the cross line.

Many large and medium-sized factories had internal rail systems, often with purpose-built industrial 0-4-0 tank locos to work them. Finished products were transferred to rail within the factory limits. Items too large for the railway loading gauge were seen on the streets, such as the huge industrial boilers produced by John Thompson Ltd. of Ettingshall, Bilston, which were hauled to their destinations, near or far, by one of the firm's large traction engines. A sight such as this was exceptional in every sense.

One rail-served company, typical of its type, was the timber yard belonging to two brothers, Donald Thomas and Percy John Powell. It was situated on the north side of the Stour Valley Line, between Monument Lane station and the carriage sidings. As the firm expanded, it grew too large for its original premises in Cambridge St. (near the back of the present Repertory Theatre), moving to Monument Lane in 1929. It provided employment for about two dozen workmen. In 1930 Donald Powell's son, also named Donald, joined the company as a ledger clerk. His photographs and memories, together with a lifelong interest in signalling, have helped to illustrate this and other features in this book. There were two main timber sheds, an open Dutch barn for storage, and a machine shop/saw mill. The yard was served by a siding which shared the approach tracks to the carriage sidings, and it had a capacity of up to 12 wagons. Much of the timber consisted of rough-sawn redwoods and softwoods from the Soviet Union and the Baltic states. It was stacked in the open. Planed timber arrived in sheeted wagons and was stored in the barn. Powell's also handled Scotch fir, used for fencing, which required treating in the yard's creosote vat. There were no mechanical aids for removing timber from the railway wagons.

A consignment of up to twelve wagons would take the yards nine 'stackers' up to four days to unload. If they took longer, preventing release of the wagons back to the railway, Powell's were required to pay a financial penalty, known as demurage. Some customers with large orders were supplied direct, as the timber was transferred directly from the rail wagons to the firm's own lorries for same day delivery. Wagons for the yard were brought in by the early morning Wolverhampton-Monument Lane pick-up goods, which propelled them off the main line and through the throat of the carriage sidings, where they were left for one of the two local shunting engines to draw them forward into the yard's own siding. All this by 7am! The operation was reversed after 6pm, as necessary. At busy periods full wagons had to be held in the general goods yard, sometimes for days, until there was space in Powell's siding.

The timber yard had two very remunerative contracts. At a time when thousands of council homes were being built throughout the city, Powell's provided the Scotch fir fencing for use on the estates. Birchwood was also supplied to the tramways department for use as the longitudinal 'ribs' which ran the full length of every tramcar floor, along the aisles. This wood was also used for the boards suspended from the bottom of each tram bodyside, almost down to the ground, the 'lifeguards'. There were smaller sized products, some of which found their way into childrens' Christmas stockings. The Great Western, more than any other railway, manufactured all sorts of items that were useful tools in its never-ending appetite for favourable publicity. These included wooden jig-saw puzzles of some of its famous trains, made at the Harborne factory of the Chad Valley Toy Company, with wood supplied by Powell's Timber Yard. On a few occasions the young Don was required to take samples of three and five-ply wood to the factory before they placed a new order. He would step direct from the yard, over the track and onto the station platform, to wait for the Harborne Express. However, this was the early 1930s, and the outlook for that particular train was bleak . . .

The Dutch barn seen in the publicity shot is to the right on this picture, which was taken from the roof of the adjacent machine mill about 1929. A rake of wagons awaits unloading, while a 4-6-2 'Prince' tank marshalls coaches. Beyond the station platform, behind the railway boundary fence, lies the 'Main Line' canal, linking Birmingham with Wolverhampton, which Thomas Telford engineered in the 1820s.   *(Don Powell)*

Ex-Midland Railway 0-6-0 No.3147 at Water Orton East Junction with a beer train from Burton-on-Trent, 3rd June 1925. The train is leaving the old line, via Whitacre. The Kingsbury - Water Orton Direct Line, opened in 1909, curves away to the left. The wooden beer barrels, manufactured to a centuries-old design, are being conveyed in a variety of three, five and seven planked wagons, some of which carry the initials LMS. The locomotive, power classification 2F, was built to a design of Samuel Waite Johnson dating from 1878.

(W.Leslie Good; Roger Carpenter collection)

The transportation of a historic item of rail freight - nobody realised just how historic or tragic when this photograph was taken on 1st May 1911. The centre anchor of the "RMS Titanic" was manufactured by Noah Hingley & Co. of Netherton and it is seen here en route from the works for the start of its rail journey at Dudley Port. Weighing 16.8 tons and designed to take a strain of 350 tons, it was drawn by a team of no fewer than twenty heavy horses. *(courtesy of Dudley Archives & Local History Centre)*

A member of the "Hall" class takes a southbound empty stock train through Bordesley. When Moor Street opened to goods traffic in 1914, livestock traffic, seen here, continued to be handled at the old goods depot at Bordesley. This view was taken from the Camp Hill line, the original route of the Midland Railway between Bristol and Birmingham. Although the scene is pure Great Western, it dates from 1955, when the Clean Air Act and the high rise buildings in the city centre were still in the future. *(Roger Carpenter collection)*

A member of the 1898 "Bulldog" Class, 4-4-0 No.3442 "Bullfinch", enters Birmingham Snow Hill with four six-wheeled tanks, the Dorrington milk train, on 5th June 1937.
(L. Hanson)

The rebuilt station at Great Barr opened in March 1899. A mixed goods trundles through, about 1920, hauled by Webb coal tank No. 3715.
(Roger Carpenter collection)

A Deeley 0-6-0 3F freight loco of 1906 design, No.3817, comes off the slow line at Halesowen Junction. The vans contain car parts and are bound for what was then the Austin Works. This site is now occupied by Longbridge station. 29th May 1935. *(Don Powell)*

ASTON JUNCTION, ASTON GOODS, AND WINDSOR STREET.

Worked as a Station Yard in accordance with Rules 87 to 89 inclusive of the Book of Rules. Also special instructions shewn in Central District Appendix.

Work Days. STATIONS. Down Trains.

	1	2	3	4	5	6	7	8	9	10	11	12	13	14	15	16
	Goods to Bescot.	Goods to Aston Junction.	Goods to Bescot.			Empty Mineral to Wichnor.	Goods to Aston Jct.	Goods to Stechford.	Goods to Stechford.	Mineral to Monument Lane.	Empty Mineral to Wichnor.	Goods to Curzon Street.		Fast Goods to Bescot.		
			192					244	244	170		186		313		
	M	M	M					S	SO			S		S		
Windsor Street dep	a.m. 1 30	a.m. 2 35	a.m. 3 15	...	...	a.m. 5 0	a.m. 8 50	a.m. 9 25	a.m. 9 50	a.m. 10 15	a.m. 10 30	a.m. 11 0 C	...	p.m. 12 35	...	...
Aston Junc. arr	1 35	2 40	3 20	...	...	5 5	8 55	9 30	9 55	10 21	10 39	11 10	...	12 42	...	...

Work Days. STATIONS. Down Trains.

	17	18	19	20	21	22	23	24	25	26	27	28	29	30	31
	Goods to Bescot.	Mineral to Aston Loco. Shed.	Empty Mineral to Wichnor.	Express Goods to Bescot.	Express Goods to Stechford.	Goods to Robinson's Sdg.	Express Goods to Stechford.		Goods to Aston Jct.	Express Goods to Curzon Street.		Goods to Bescot.	Goods to Stechford.	Express Goods to Liverpool.	Sundays. Goods to Bescot.
	313		163	173	38	45	45			45		24	174	25	
	SO	S		SO	SO	SO	S		SO			S			
Windsor Street. dep	p.m. 1 40	p.m. 3 15	p.m 3 35	p.m. 4 30	p.m. 6 30	p.m. 7 5	p.m. 7 20	...	p.m. 8 5	p.m. 8 5	...	p.m. 9 35	p.m. 9 55	p.m. 10 50	a.m. 12 30
Aston Junc. arr	1 45	3 20	3 42	4 35	6 40	7 10	7 25	...	8 10	8 17	...	9 48	10 0	10 55	12 35

The October 1921 working time-table, showing trains leaving Windsor Street Goods. It also shows some slight incompatibility between a good modern photocopier and a historic document with a stiff spine! *(courtesy of Dan Pawson)*

LOCOS ON SHED

At a time when thousands of Birmingham's factory and household chimneys still belched forth tons of smoke and soot every day, the opportunities for a clear sunny photograph were rare indeed. This is Monument Lane engine shed, about 1920. Two examples of the work of Francis Webb can be seen, first and fourth from the left. Webb was succeeded by George Whale in 1903 and a member of his 4-4-0 "Precedent" Class stands on the right. These express passenger locos were his first design, intended to provide more power and dimish the amount of double heading necessary. Whale resigned in 1909 and was succeeded by C. J. Bowen-Cooke, two of whose engines are sandwiched between those of Webb.
(National Railway Museum)

Bushbury shed, Wolverhampton in LMS days, with a fine mixture of ex-LNWR locos.
(courtesy of Wolverhampton Archives & Local Studies and Alex Chatwin)

A splendid array of locos at Bescot, 26th May 1931, Super D No.9039 (unrebuilt) and Webb tank No.7582, to the fore. The shed is to the left, the familiar Wellman-Smith coaling plant was not built until 1933. *(L. Hanson)*

An interesting view of Bescot across the turntable well, May 1938. *(Alex Chatwin collection)*

The roundhouse at Bournville. Locos (l.to r.) are Stanier 2-6-2 tank No.178; Fowler 4-4-0 3-cylinder compound No.1064; Kirtley 0-6-0 of 1868 vintage No.22863; Johnson simple 4-4-0 No.439; Johnson 0-6-0 No.3583; Deeley 4-4-0 compound No.1039. August 1947.

(Kidderminster Railway Museum)

Engine sheds could be found in the most unlikely places! This is the LNWR establishment at Tipton, complete with 0-6-0 tank loco, in 1936.

(W. A. Camwell; Roger Carpenter collection)

A colourful poster announcing the opening of Perry Barr Greyhound Stadium, conveniently reached by rail. Were they really expecting two thousand cars . . . in 1928?

(National Railway Museum)

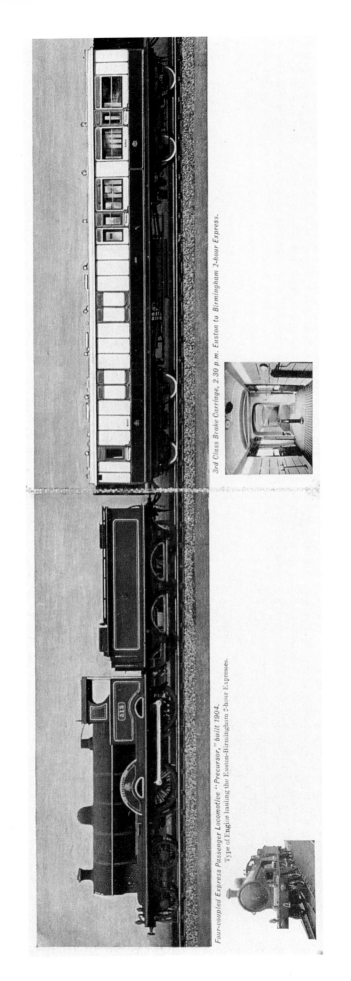

Four-coupled Express Passenger Locomotive "Precursor," built 1904.
Type of Engine hauling the Euston-Birmingham 2-hour Expresses.

3rd Class Brake Carriage, 2.30 p.m. Euston to Birmingham 2-hour Express.

3rd Class Carriage, 2.30 p.m. Euston to Birmingham 2-hour Express.

3rd Class Carriage, 2.30 p.m. Euston to Birmingham 2-hour Express.

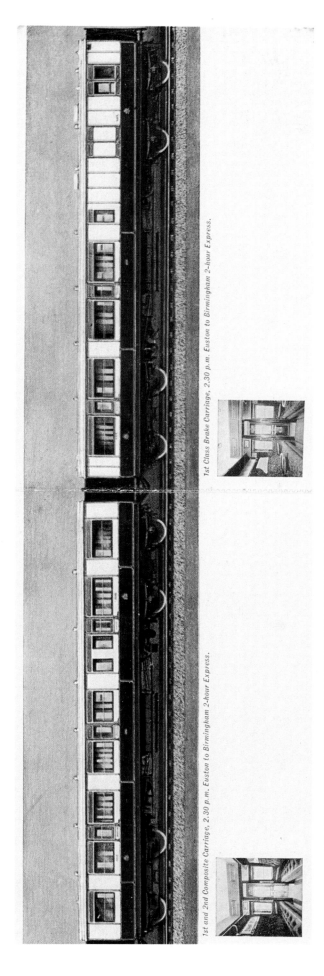

1st and 2nd Composite Carriage, 2.30 p.m. Euston to Birmingham '2-hour Express.

1st Class Brake Carriage, 2.30 p.m. Euston to Birmingham 2-hour Express.

An attractive six-card set, unused and still intact, depicting one of the London & North Western 2-Hour New Street-Euston expresses. These cards were first published at the introduction of the service in 1905.

(courtesy of Paul King)

The Queen's Hotel entrance to New Street station, about 1905. For a busy station with such an impressive roof, the main entrance was amazingly pokey. The entrance gates first performed the same function at Curzon Street, the original terminus of the London & Birmingham Railway. The black and white version of this card has a group of boys loitering innocently in the bottom left hand corner – eliminated from the more expensive colour edition.

(courtesy of Paul King)

QUEENS & NORTH WESTERN HOTEL, BIRMINGHAM.
ADJOINING NEW ST. STATION L.& N.W.RAILWAY.

NEW STATIONS, 1935-1940, AS SEEN IN MORE RECENT YEARS

1935. A three-car Western region dmu leaves The Lakes Halt with the 4.15pm from Birmingham Moor Street to Henley-in-Arden on 25th August 1962.
(Michael Mensing)

1936. No. 4905 "Barton Hall" ambles through Whitlock's End Halt with a northbound freight on Sunday 8th July 1962.
(Michael Mensing)

1939. Made in Birmingham. A three-car Birmingham Railway Carriage & Wagon Co. dmu leaves Lea Hall with the 1.29pm local service from New Street to Coventry and Rugby, 1st September 1964. The period platform lamp posts carry red totems, electrification is on the way, and the rosebay willow herb adds a welcome dash of colour. *(Michael Mensing)*

1940. Loco No.E3019 (Class 81) in original Electric Blue livery, speeds through Canley Halt with the 10.27am Manchester Piccadilly-Euston, 24th August 1968. *(Michael Mensing)*

"What about the workers?" used to be the cry. The workers were sometimes short-changed by the railways, judging by both photographs on this page. A 0-6-0 pannier tank of the 1501 Class, No.1749, has a half cab offering little protection to the workers who form the foot-plate crew. Those travelling to the Austin car plant at Longbridge also have to endure the primitive comforts of an ancient coach, seen at Halesowen early in 1949.

(Colour-Rail/ the late Patrick Whitehouse)

Pre-war commuters at Leamington Spa travelled in quaint vintage rolling stock from an antique station, judging by this 1935 photograph of 4916 "Crumlin Hall", just arrived with a train from Snow Hill.

(Colour-Rail)

BUILT IN THE 1920s . . .

136 tons of living steam, in the shape of 6012 "King Edward VI", thunders through Widney Manor with the 2.35pm Birkenhead-Paddington on 10th May 1958, an unforgettable sight for those fortunate enough to have seen such a thing. *(Michael Mensing)*

GROWING OLD GRACEFULLY IN THE 1930s . . .

The "Prince of Wales" class of express passenger loco was designed by Charles Bowen-Cooke for the LNWR in 1911. By the time this photograph was taken, in 1938, surviving members of the class were employed on lighter duties. Here No. 25673 "Lusitania" stands at the narrow island Platform 2 at Birmingham New Street with a semi-fast for Manchester (London Road) via Stoke-on-Trent.

(Colour-Rail/the late Patrick Whitehouse)

This 1938 poster by the LMS is interesting but disappointing. Artistically, the style and colour of the heading is pleasant, but the rest of the poster clashes with it. Of greater interest to the serious punter is the speed of the train, or lack of it, at a time when the fastest expresses completed the journey between Euston and New Street in 1 hour 55 minutes. The onward connection to Bromford Bridge racecourse station, a mere five miles distant, can only be described as pathetic. At least the return fare (which translates as 62½p) was reasonable. The racecourse now lies under part of the Castle Vale housing estate.

(National Railway Museum)

CHAPTER FOUR : 1930-1939

[Diary : Notes : Made in Birmingham : The Harborne Express]

Diary

1930

First "Patriot" locos built by LMS.

2-6-2 tank locos (3P), designed by Fowler and numbered 1-70, built by LMS.

March 31st – Passenger service, Aldridge-Brownhills Watling Street withdrawn. Brownhills closed completely, Walsall Wood, remained open for goods.

April 24th – Goods service south of Maxstoke, on Whitacre-Hampton line, closed.

July 28th – Somerset Road station, Birmingham West Suburban Line, closed completely.

1931

January 5th – Passenger services over ex-Midland line between Walsall and Wolverhampton withdrawn. Intermediate stations remained open for goods.

May 18th – Icknield Port Road station closed completely.

December 25th – The Hawthorns Halt opened to serve West Bromwich Albion's football ground. On this Christmas Day morning seventeen special trains converged on the station for the 'Baggies' match against Birmingham City - 'Blues' won by the only goal.

1932

October 29th – Wombourn line passenger service withdrawn.

1934

First "Black Five" and "Jubilee" locos built by LMS.

March 25th – "Kings" used on bridge tests on newly quadrupled section between Olton and Lapworth.

July 9th – Express diesel railcar service began, Birmingham Snow Hill-Cardiff General.

November 24th – Passenger services ceased on the Harborne branch.

1935

First Standard 2-8-0 (8F) heavy freight locos built by LMS.

June 3rd – The Lakes Halt, with very short platforms, opened on the North Warwickshire Line, mainly for the benefit of fishermen. The 'lakes', at Earlswood, are reservoirs which feed the Stratford Canal.

1936

First "Grange" locos built by GWR.

July 6th – Whitlock's End Halt opened on the North Warwickshire Line.

1937

First "Princess Coronation" Pacific locos (sometimes known as 'Semis' or 'Lizzies') built by LMS.

1938

First "Manor" locos built by GWR.

1939

May 1st – Goods service withdrawn on the last section of the Whitacre-Hampton line and Maxstoke station (formerly named 'Coleshill') closed. This was not quite the end for a railway that had started out as a main line. There were high grade sand pits at Bannerley Common, two miles north of Hampton. They were enlarged in the autumn of 1940 as the sand was needed for construction of RAF runways. This generated three trains per week. Most of the line was lifted in 1952, with short sections kept at both ends to store crippled wagons.

May 1st – Lea Hall opened.

August 3rd – Brindley Heath station, between Hednesford and Rugeley Town, opened for RAF personnel using the nearby base. Opened for general public use on August 26th.

September 1st – In common with other large conurbations, the railways began evacuating children from Birmingham to areas less at risk from bombing.

September 3rd – Britain and France declare war on Germany.

September 25th – Early wartime cutbacks in passenger services on this date were closure of the New Street Circle service via Handsworth Wood, and withdrawal of the Snow Hill-Bristol expresses.

Notes

During the 1930s the LMS excelled in the production of first rate steam locomotives. Henry Fowler's swansong came in 1930, with the appearance of the 4-6-0 "Patriot" Class, sometimes known as 'Baby Scots'. Fowler's other design of 1930, the 2-6-2 tank engines, numbered 1-70, were underpowered, a disappointment after his 2-6-4 tanks of 1927. Some 2-6-2s were based at Ryecroft for working suburban traffic.

William Stanier became Chief Mechanical Engineer of the LMS in 1935, bringing with him many years' experience in senior management from Swindon, where he had started his career in 1892. He was his own man, who had a sense of the ordered way of doing things that came from long years with the GWR. The loco types he produced included the "Jubilee" (1934), "Princess Coronation" (1937), "Black Five" (1934) and the 2-8-0 (8F) heavy freight loco of 1935. The last two types in particular were familiar sights in the West Midlands, from the 1930s until their demise in the 1960s. The "Black Fives" were considered to be the best mixed traffic locos built by the LMS, handling both express passenger and assorted freight workings with equal ease.

Over 500 were built. The 2-8-0 freight locos were also numerous and efficient, with a large superheated boiler, small driving wheels for added power at slow speeds 'with a load on', and a boiler pressure of 225lb./sq.in.

In contrast, the Great Western seemed to produce little of note. The 80 members of the "Grange" Class (1936) and the 20 "Manors" (1938) seemed to be smaller and less powerful clones of earlier types, handy for mixed traffic, or for taking the furthest portions of holiday expresses onto lines where "Kings" and "Castles" dared not venture. Yet, the most forward looking design of the decade was the GWR express diesel railcar. Three such vehicles began running between Snow Hill and Cardiff in July 1934. With two 130 brake-horse-power engines and a maximum speed of 80mph, the journey time between the two cities was reduced to less than $2\frac{1}{2}$ hours, a saving of 35 minutes over steam, and the service was an instant success. By 1935 there were seven cars running, some based at Worcester, Oxford and Leamington. The "Railway Magazine" for July 1939 published statistics showing how efficient the railcars were. By 1938 they numbered 18, and between them they were scheduled to run 22,530 miles per week, or 3% of the total GWR passenger train miles! Passengers carried rose from 641,000 in 1936 to 983,000 in 1938 and the annual average mileage for each car was 53,196. Although a familiar sight at Snow Hill, Dudley, etc., Droitwich saw more railcar workings than any other station, with 20 calling daily. So far, the railcars had been single units, but in 1939 an order was placed for 20 two-car units. They were completed during the early part of the war.

In the first weeks of 1934, quadrupling of the line was completed between Olton and Lapworth. The strength of the new bridges was tested in spectacular fashion on the morning of Sunday 25th March. Four "Kings" were assembled – 6001, 6014, 6017 and 6005. The first two were coupled together without load, the others hauled just two carriages. The two pairs of locos at first crawled, at 2mph, abreast of each other across a given bridge while the vertical deflections of its girders were measured, with instruments, by men positioned on the roadway underneath. Further tests followed, at speeds up to 62mph. There were twelve such runs over double-tracked bridges, and four more test runs by 6001 and 6005 on two single track bridges which carried the down relief line:-

"The pairs of locomotives were drawn dead level as they approached the bridge, the exhausts rising quite 30ft. in the brilliant sunlight above each of the four chimneys, to the accompaniement of a deafening roar. The nominal test conditions were 500 tons weight and 60mph; in actual fact the four locomotives and tenders weighed 542 tons full and in various runs speeds of up to 62mph were attained . . . Railway enthusiasts from considerable distances, and other spectators also, might have been attracted had the fact been made public that these tests were to take place . . ."

("Railway Magazine" June 1934).

Two halts and one station, which opened on new sites in the 1930s, are still in business today. The station at Lea Hall, opened in 1939, was built to serve an area of new local authority housing in east Birmingham. The buildings are of reinforced concrete. This material had been used to new and daring effect earlier in the decade in the penguin enclosures of both Regent's Park and Dudley zoos. Unlike earlier concrete stations on the LMS (eg: Apsley, Meols), the canopies of the platform buildings did not require the support of heavy beams above. Just a thin and elegant wafer of concrete shelters waiting passengers, a little appreciated fact at what is now a heavily over-vandalised station. The line is in a shallow cutting and the booking office is on the footbridge. This was intended to minimise disruption when the planned quadrupling between Birmingham and Coventry took place (sadly, it never did) and both platforms could easily be converted to islands.

As for Coventry itself, the city was always dominated by one railway company – LNWR, then LMS – with very limited running rights for the Midland Railway before the Grouping. It was the largest city in the West Midlands where one company enjoyed a virtual monopoly, although such niceties were swept aside on summer Saturdays. As peace gave way to war one correspondent informed the "Railway Magazine" (September 1939), that holidaymakers returning to the city did so in trains from all four companies – LMS of course; LNER, probably from Yarmouth via the Midland & Great Northern line; GWR from Weston-super-Mare and Southern from Ramsgate. However, all these trains were "hauled by LMS engines".

Un-named "Patriot" No.5514 leaves Birmingham New Street for the Stour Valley line, 7th May 1938. Ex-Midland 3-cylinder Compound 4-4-0 No.1164 can be glimpsed at Platform 2. The good condition of the loco is not matched by that of the overall roof.

(L. Hanson)

A member of the 4300 Class, No. 6314, heads a Birmingham-Oxford train over Lapworth troughs, about 1929.

(courtesy of Solihull Education, Libraries and Arts)

6020 "King Henry IV" passes Olton with the 5.10pm from Paddington to Birkenhead, 26th August 1959. Twenty five years earlier, four "Kings" working together had tested the bridges between Olton and Lapworth in spectacular fashion. *(Michael Mensing)*

Made in Birmingham

The building of railway rolling stock in the West Midlands dates back to 1845, when Joseph Wright, who belonged to the third generation of a family of road coach builders, established a works at Saltley, near the present day site of Metro Cammell in Washwood Heath. "Joseph Wright & Sons" changed its name to the "Metropolitan Railway Carriage & Wagon Co.Ltd." in 1862; today's establishment is a direct descendant of this company, having opened on the present site in 1912.

By 1900 carriage and wagon building was at its peak, with Britain constructing two thirds of the world's passenger coaches. In the early years of the century, Metropolitan Amalgamated, as it was then known, employed 14,000 men, most of them in Saltley, Oldbury and Wednesbury. Always at the forefront of new technology, the company built large numbers of bodies for rail motors, mainly for export, from 1903. In 1902 an order for new deep level 'tube' stock was received from the Central London Railway. The West Midlands' other main rolling stock builder, the Birmingham Railway Carriage & Wagon Co. (BRCW), shared this order, supplying 40 cars to Metropolitan's 24. Earlier electric trains on the Underground were pulled by locomotives; these had the motors incorporated into the carriage frames and were thus the first multiple units in Europe. Expansion of the Underground after the First World War resulted in further orders, for Bakerloo and District line stock.

Metropolitan had always exported, and the 1920s saw an upsurge in orders from Europe, as builders there were generally slower to recover from the effects of war and were loath to accept payment by instalments. So, Metropolitan built 15 Pullman cars specifically for the "Fleche d'Or" ("Golden Arrow"), as well as 40 further Pullmans and 60 sleeping cars. BRCW delivered Wagons-Lits sleeping cars to France between 1926 and 1929, receiving their final payment in 1951!

Between the two world wars, Metro Cammell secured important orders from around the world, especially from countries where the rail network was still expanding, such as China, India, Argentina, Brazil and South Africa.

At the start of the world recession which followed the Wall Street Crash of 1929, Metro Cammell adapted and diversified in order to survive. Its experience with rail was useful in building steel-framed bus bodies and, between 1933 and 1936, lightweight tramcars for Edinburgh and Johannesburg. The Southern Railway was electrifying its London-Brighton main line and in 1932 Metro Cammell built three 5-car electric Pullman sets for the new "Brighton Belle", plus 23 individual Pullman coaches for use on other Southern electric services. The "Brighton Belle" ran until 1972 and some of the cars are still running today, in the "Orient Express".

1938 can only be described as a huge year for the order books. The LMS required nineteen 3-car sets (Class 503 in British Rail days) for its newly-electrified Liverpool-Wirrall lines, and the LNER needed sixty-four 2-car sets for its North Tyneside services. This work was shared with BRCW, leaving Metro Cammell to concentrate its resources on the order for no fewer than 751 motor carriages for the London Underground. They classified their stock by year, and this '1938' stock, the first with a smooth modern profile, particularly on the roof, established the accepted shape of the London Underground train for the next forty years. The trailer cars for the same order, 370 in all, were built by BRCW. In 1938 Metro Cammell also built the prestige 12-car "Blue Train" for the 3'6" gauge South African Railways, although prior to 1946 it was known as the "Union Limited".

During the Second World War, Metro Cammell was the country's largest single supplier of tanks, devoting 80% of its capacity to their production. They also produced armoured car bodies, radar vehicles and rocket projectors, plus a limited number of rail wagons for the Ministry of Supply and the US Army.

After the war, rail production was quickly resumed. Some Pullman cars, which had been stored on site during the war, were refurbished and used on the "Devon Belle", introduced by the Southern Railway between Waterloo, Plymouth and Illfracombe in the summer of 1947. The twelve coaches for the train in which the Royal Family toured South Africa in 1947 were built by Metro Cammell at the Old Park Works, Wednesbury. An excellent model of one such coach is (at the time of writing) on display at the Birmingham Science Museum.

BRCW closed in 1963, but what is now GEC Alsthom Metro-Cammell continues to play a major part in producing railway rolling stock, both for home and abroad.

A two-plank wagon built at Saltley for the 3 foot gauge Isle of Man Railway in 1923. Its weight, when empty, was 3 tons 2 hundredweights 3 quarters (c.3.2tonnes). The rump of this railway is now a summer only tourist line, but before the Second World War it ran passenger and freight services all year round. Around 1920 its freight stock of 175 assorted wagons and vans outnumbered the 115 passenger carriages.

(courtesy of GEC Alsthom Metro-Cammell)

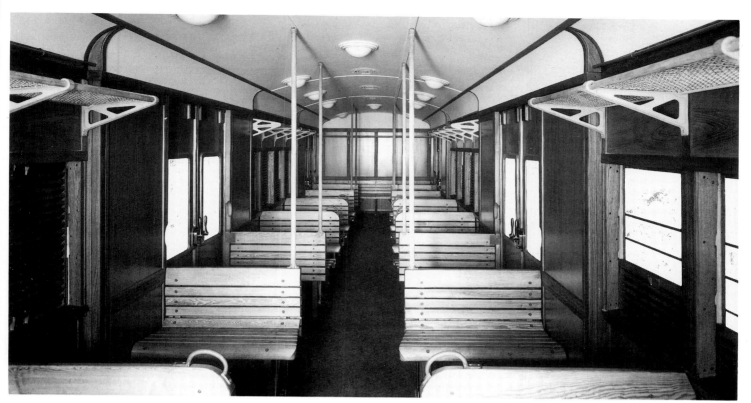

In 1929 Metro-Cammell received an order from the South Indian Railway for rolling stock for Madras's metre gauge suburban system, which was being electrified. The stock was built at Saltley. The third class accommodation, seen here, was rugged. Severe overcrowding has always been endemic on urban lines in India and the weather in Madras is hot all year round, with intense humidity during the midsummer monsoon. During that season any rail journey becomes a sauna on wheels but at least the wooden seating is less sweaty than the upholstery of first and second class!
(courtesy of GEC Alsthom Metro-Cammell)

Interior of a first class smoking carriage built for the electrification of the Wirrall suburban lines of the LMS during 1937. The roof maps show the newly energised routes linking Liverpool with New Brighton and West Kirby, while a dotted line indicates the 'Dockers' Umbrella', the Liverpool Overhead Railway.
(courtesy of GEC Alsthom Metro-Cammell)

Harborne to Birmingham.

NOTE.—Harborne Junction and Harborne Station—Single Line worked by Electric Train Staff Block System in accordance with Appendix IX. of the Book of Rules and Regulations, with an intermediate Crossing Station at Rotton Park Road. Staff Stations, Monument Lane Station (Ticket Collectors' Office), Rotton Park Road Station, and Harborne Signal Box.

UP STATIONS. — Week days.

Distance from Harborne	STATIONS.	1	5	6	7	9	11	13	15	17	20	21	23	25
		Pas	Pas	Pas	Pas	Pas	Pas	Pas	Pas	Pas	Empt Goods	Pas SO	Pas SO	Pas S
		a.m.	a.m.	a.m.	a.m.	a.m.	a.m.	a.m.	a.m.	a.m.	a.m.	p.m.	p.m.	p.m.
—	Harborne ....depart	5 36	6 20	7 10	7 28	8 5	8 20	8 33	8 51	9 14	11 45	12 47	12 52	1 46
1	Hagley Road ....,,	5 40	6 24	7 14	7 32	8 9	8 24	8 37	8 55	9 18	S	12 51	12 56	1 50
1¼	Mitchells & Butlers' Sd. ,,	...	...	...	...	...	...	...	...	...	11§59	...	12 58	1 52
1¾	Rotton Park Road {arrive	5 42	6 26	7 16	7 34	8 11	8 26	8 39	8 57	9 20	12 0	12 55	1 1	1 53
	{depart	5 43	6 27	7 18	7 35	8 12	8 27	8 40	8 58	9 22				
2¼	Icknield Port Road ....,,	5 46	6 30	7 21	7 38	8 15	8 30	8 43	9 1	9 25	12 58	1 4	1 56	
2½	Harborne Junction ....pass	5 48	6 31	7 23	7 39	8 16	8 31	8 45	9 3	9 27	12 10	1 1	1 7	1 59
2¾	Monument Lane {arrive	5 49	6 32	7 24	7 40	8 17	8 32	8 46	9 4	9 28		1 5	1 12	2 2
	{depart	5 52	6 36	7 28	7 43	8 20	8 35	8 49	9 8	9 32			1 17	2 2
3¾	BIRMINGHAM (New St.) arr	5 56	6 40	7 32	7 47	8 24	8 39	8 53	9 12	9 36		1 10		2 6

UP STATIONS. — Week days. / Sundays.

STATIONS.	27	29		30	35	36	38	40	42	44	45	46	48	49	50	51	52	53
	Pas SO	Pas	Goods 193 S SO	Pas	Goods 194 S	Goods 194 SO	Pas	Pas	Pas	Pas	Pas	Pas	Goods 193 S					
	p.m.	p.m.	p.m.	p.m.	p.m.	p.m.	p.m.	p.m.	p.m.	p.m.	p.m.	p.m.	p.m.					
Harborne ....depart	1 54	2 12	2 40	2 55	...	...	4 37	6 25	7 20	8 16	9 6	10 5	11 20					
Hagley Road ....,,	1 58	2 16		2 59	...	...	4 41	6 29	7 24	8 20	9 10	10 9	11 38					
Mitchells & Butlers' Sd. ,,	...	...		...	3 40	3 53	...	...	...	...	...	...						
Rotton Park Road {arrive	2 0	2 19	2§47	3 1	3§42	3§55	4 43	6 31	7 26	8 22	9 12	10 11	11§39					
{depart	2 2	2 21	2 48	3 2	3 43	3 56	4 44	6 35	7 29	8 24	9 13	10 13	11 40					
Icknield Port Road ....,,	2 6	2 24		3 5			4 47	6 38	7 32	8 27	9 16	10 16						
Harborne Junction ....pass	2 7	2 25	2 55	3 6	3 51	4 6	4 48	6 40	7 33	8 28	9 17	10 17	11 52					
Monument Lane {arrive	2 8	2 26	2 57	3 7	3 53	4 6	4 49	6 41	7 35	8 29	9 18	10 18	11 55					
{depart	2 11	2 30		3 11			4 52	6 45	7 39	8 32	9 21	10 21						
BIRMINGHAM (New St.) arr	2 15	2 34		3 15			4 56	6 50	7 43	8 36	9 25	10 25						

All the trains from Harborne to Birmingham are shown here, including the late night goods and the workings from Mitchells & Butlers. This was the working time-table for October 1921.

(courtesy of Dan Pawson)

The Harborne Express

Until the middle of the nineteenth century, Harborne was a small Staffordshire village centred on its ancient parish church of St. Peter. The building of the railway ensured that it rapidly became a suburb of Birmingham, although even today some local people refer to its centre as 'the village'. In 1865 a line was planned from Birmingham through Harborne, to a junction with a projected Halesowen & Bromsgrove Railway at Lapal. At the Birmingham end it was to have access to New Street via a junction near Monument Lane. The branch was to continue north, bridging the Stour Valley line, until it joined the Great Western main line to Snow Hill as well, via a junction near Soho. As with so many railway schemes, these original intentions were too ambitious for either the finance available or the likely traffic, so they were scaled down. The Halesowen & Bromsgrove became simply the Halesowen Railway, as described in Chapter Three, opening in 1883.

The Harborne Line, as built, was just a 2½ mile long branch from Harborne Junction, near Monument Lane, with no link to the Great Western. It opened on 10th August 1874, with stations at Icknield Port Road, Rotton Park Road, Hagley Road and Harborne. The journey into New Street, which according to the working time-tables was a distance of 3⅞ miles, took about twenty minutes. Rotton Park and Hagley Road were very much in the country, with few houses nearby, and the station at Harborne itself was almost surrounded by fields when the line opened. Streets of neat villas soon appeared – many of them are still there – and Harborne became part of the new City of

Birmingham in 1891. One small practical benefit of this was the construction of two short sidings in the goods yard, for wagons carrying rock salt to grit the local roads in icy weather.

Growth and prosperity, plus the crucial fact that trams never reached Harborne, meant that the number of trains each way expanded from six in 1874, to eighteen in 1883, when an hourly service began, with trains leaving Harborne's newly lengthened platform every hour from 06.45 until 22.45, except for three variants during the morning peak. This was a very early example of regular interval working. The number of trains rose to a maximum of thirty in 1910, making this the busiest suburban line into Birmingham, New Street or Snow Hill. The service was such that city businessmen, and pupils attending King Edward's High School in New Street, could nip home for lunch every day. Trains were normally eight coaches long, hauled by Webb tank engines shedded at Monument Lane.

Improvements were carried out to cope with the volume of passengers. The original station at Icknield Port Road had a short platform sandwiched between the two overbridges of Barford Road and Icknield Port Road itself. It was replaced by a new station south of its road, with longer platforms, in 1897. To fit more trains into the time-table, a passing loop was provided at Rotton Park Road, where the side platform was adapted to become an island, in 1903. The new track, on the north side of the island platform, obliterated the footpath access from the road, so an awkward looking wooden trestle walkway and footbridge was provided on the south side. Insofar as signalling was concerned, Rotton Park Road was only a block post before 1903,

A train from Birmingham New Street approaching journey's end at Harborne, one day in 1906. Everything appears to be well cared for.
(Don Powell collection)

Harborne station during the last month of the passenger service, November 1934. An ex-LNWR Webb tank engine poses with a rake of private owner wagons, including one from West Cannock Colliery, Hednesford. The Chad Valley toy factory lies to the right. The original Harborne Railway signal box, visible in the top picture, was replaced by one of LNWR pattern in 1920.
(W. A. Camwell : Don Powell collection)

allowing two trains on the branch at a time, so long as they were both heading in the same direction! The line was at first worked on the 'one engine in steam' principle and later by the 'staff and ticket' system. This was succeeded by the 'electric train staff' system – the staff being batons which were issued by signalmen to the footplate crew as their authority to proceed onto the single line. They were electrically locked into their apparatus until needed and could not be released for issue if the line was already occupied. (At Rotton Park Road this apparatus, together with the signal levers, was housed in a part of the station buildings, as there was no separate signal box.) The batons were collected, on down journeys, from Monument Lane, exchanged at Rotton Park Road and surrendered at Harborne signal box. The two tracks through Harborne station combined to focus on the thirty-foot long turntable, the last feature at the very end of the branch. There was just a short emergency stub beyond it, with no other tracks leading off. The turntable was removed in 1943. A second platform was in existence at Harborne between 1901 and 1911 but it had no connection with the rest of the station. It was devoid of buildings and appears never to have been used. A footbridge was built in 1908, but its purpose was to provide direct access to Park Hill Road and other streets rapidly being developed west of the station. (The area between Park Hill and Lordswood roads was mostly fields in 1905; by 1914 the present day street pattern was established.) The second platform was removed in 1911 and replaced by more sidings.

Hagley Road had its own sidings, used mainly for the receipt of house coal, and at Harborne there was a siding to the Chad Valley Toy Factory. The largest source of freight traffic was Mitchells & Butlers Brewery at Cape Hill, just south of Rotton Park. The LNWR agreed to a rail connection in 1904. The branch was half a mile long, leading to an extensive system within the brewery, which covered an area of 50 acres and employed over one thousand men. M&B went on to become the largest brewery in Europe. The internal railway opened in 1907 and from then on virtually everything required by M&B – machinery, barley, hops, bottles and even the labels for the bottles – arrived by rail. The M&B system, entered via a gate from the Harborne branch, was worked by the brewery's own 0-4-0 locomotives. Most unusual of these was a geared tank engine built by Aveling & Porter of Rochester, supplied new in 1907 and named "John Barleycorn". It was replaced by a conventional saddle tank, "John Barleycorn II", bought new from Andrew Barclay of Kilmarnock as late as 1951. An old contractor's engine, of 1889 vintage and named "Beatrice", was in service between 1907 and 1929. "Boniface" replaced "Beatrice" and remained until the M&B system closed on 31st March 1962. (The end of rail traffic to the brewery was a major factor in the decision to close the Harborne branch completely the following year.)

Unlike the vast majority of minor companies the Harborne Railway was more than just nominally independent. It had offices in London rather than Birmingham and had entered into an agreement with the LNWR when the line was opened, whereby the Harborne contributed towards the cost of the junction with the main line and the LNWR worked the line for 50% of the gross receipts. Only a tiny fraction of the other 50% went into the coffers of the Harborne or the bank accounts of its shareholders. Despite the success of the line, the small company was saddled with debts in the early days, causing it to be in the hands of the Receiver between 1879 and 1900. After that, annual dividends paid to shareholders never exceeded a modest 3%. On three occasions the LNWR tried to buy out the smaller concern, without success, and the agreement lasted until the formation of the LMS at the beginning of 1923.

The ruling gradient on the branch was 1:66, rising from the junction with the main line as far as Hagley Road and easing through Rotton Park Road to 1:224 before falling at 1:66 for the mile into Harborne, entered via a high embankment over the Chad Valley. The gradient caused at least two accidents when a goods train ran away towards the main line. In 1953 some wagons derailed and fell into the canal just before the junction, but the earlier incident, in 1905, could have been much more serious. Normally the "Railway Magazine" is noted for its accuracy, but in this report there are two errors within one sentence:-

"A train of 35 loaded trucks ran down a declivity on the LNWR, between Birmingham and Harborne on the morning of July 12th, and was partially wrecked. The engine had been detached in connection with shunting operations" (presumably at Hagley Road) *"and the waggons began to move backwards, even though the brakes were on. Howells, the guard, jumped into his van and vainly endeavoured to stop the train. The line falls for four miles(!) to Monument Road Station (that had become the name of the road, but the station remained 'Lane') and it was realised that the only alternative was to give the running train a clear course. Making a leap, the guard rolled down an embankment, and escaped with slight injury. Meanwhile, warning was telephoned to Monument Road, and the main line was cleared. The points were placed to conduct the train into a siding, and soon afterwards it broke its immense weight against some empty trucks. Wreckage was scattered in all directions."*

Despite the intensity and health of the passenger service, problems did arise. There was noise from shunting activity, some of which normally occurred late at night, when the station was free at last of passenger train movements. One writer to the "Birmingham Post" in August 1902, a season ticket holder who threatened to *"leave the neighbourhood at the earliest opportunity"*, complained that *"those of us who unfortunately reside within a short distance of the Harborne railway station and goods yard hardly know what it is to enjoy a night's uninterrupted sleep."*

More seriously, virtually nothing was done to arrest the decline that set in after the First World War. Even before that conflict the arrival of the first buses had had an impact. Passengers using the line had declined from 360,000 in 1912 to 294,000 in 1913, with a reduction in fare revenue of £791 (about 1.25p [3d] per lost passenger). As Harborne's sparse bus service improved the train service was reduced, the sort of unimaginative response to competition that virtually guarantees failure. As early as 1921 no trains left Harborne between 9.14am and 12.47pm, and there were no branch trains leaving New Street between 7.22am and 12.10pm. The worst problems occurred as inbound trains approached the junction with the main line. They were often late and unreliable because the Monument Lane signalman held them on the branch until the busy main line was clear. Once allowed onto the main line they were brought to another halt at Monument Lane station for a mandatory ticket check, which was time-consuming and tedious in a crowded non-corridor train. (New Street had no ticket barriers, so there were ticket checks for all local trains at the inner stations on its approaches.) This double frustration was the reason passengers deserted to the buses and trams in their droves, some doing so 'on the spot' by clambering out of the train held at the junction, onto the road and into a passing tramcar. By the late 1920s three carriages were sufficient for all trains. Icknield Port Road station closed on 18th May 1931, but given the frequent tram services along Dudley Road and Icknield Port Road and the fact that the trains took ten minutes to cover 1¾ miles into New Street – if they were not delayed – it is surprising that this station lasted so long. One correspondent to the "Birmingham Post" (18th May 1931)

Harborne station in November 1934, just before the withdrawal of the passenger service. The lone engine, deserted platform and dull weather are in keeping with the prevailing mood. *(courtesy of Harborne Library)*

The weather matches the mood as the first passenger train for almost sixteen years suns itself at Harborne. The Webb tank had been specially smartened up at Monument Lane for the Stephenson Locomotive Society special of 3rd June 1950. Most men who were boys at this time will recall short trousers, braces, inefficient garters which caused crinkly socks, plus mothers who wore floral-print summer dresses, and rimless glasses courtesy of the new-fangled National Health Service. The sidings contained trucks full of house coal prior to the Clean Air Act and the stack of wood on the right would seem to indicate that the Chad Valley toy factory still made use of the railway. As this was probably the first ever push-pull train on the branch the loco displays a tail light, in readiness to propel its train out of the station. *(courtesy of Harborne Library)*

commented:–

"Now that the LMS has announced the closing of Icknield Port Road station, may I suggest that this service be quickened up to 13 minutes instead of the usual 20 minutes. Surely the distance can be covered at a greater speed than the existing average of 12m.p.h." The writer signed him/herself as "20 M.P.H."

It was the lack of speed that had earlier given the train service the nickname of "Harborne Express", the subject of comic postcards and threadbare jokes in the local music halls and Christmas pantomimes. One such involved an irate ticket collector, who accused an old man with a white beard of travelling on a child's ticket, to which the gentleman replied that he had only been eleven years old when the train left Harborne.

Several fare reductions after 1931 made travelling on the line something of a bargain. By 1934 the third class return fare from Harborne to New Street was the same as a single at just 3d (1.25p). The bus fare for the same journey was 3d single or 4d for a workman's return. A first class season ticket from Harborne, for three months, cost £1/12/6d (£1.62), reduced from an earlier level of £2/2/3d (£2.11). Despite these fares, the service was no more reliable and by the autumn of 1934 Harborne station was issuing an average of just 100 tickets each day. As that worked out at only five per train, it is fair to assume that some off peak services would be setting out empty.

It was to be after the formation of British Railways before the closure of any passenger service was subject to a proper and legally binding process, giving objectors the right to appeal, with sufficient time to prepare their case. When the LMS decided that the Harborne line was to close, the end came quickly. News was leaked at the end of October 1934 and the "Evening Despatch" (31st October) gave the closure date as Saturday 24th November. "An official of the company at Euston station today said it was proposed to close down the line owing to the decline in passenger traffic and a decision would be made by the Board of Directors in a few days time. The branch line will still be open for goods . . ." Closure was recommended by the Board and a last minute appeal by a deputation of season ticket holders was informed by J. F. Brook (District Passenger Manager at New Street) that there was no hope of a reprieve.

The line, despite its decline, had become part of the folklore of Harborne and Birmingham. The last day of service saw hundreds of extra passengers anxious to take one last ride. The final "Harborne Express" left New Street at 11.08pm, with eight very crowded carriages, and many more people on Platform 1, just to see it off. The train was met by crowds at the intermediate stations. At Harborne itself the passengers soon swarmed all over the track, clambering in front of and onto the locomotive, where the scene was recorded for posterity by a flash light camera, still something of a novelty in 1934. The crowd eventually melted into the night, leaving the station to the ghosts of 60 years of season ticket holders.

General goods facilities continued to be provided at Harborne and Hagley Road. The Chad Valley toy factory leased the station buildings at Harborne. Frames Tours opened an LMS ticket agency in Harborne High Street. Passenger stock continued to use the branch, but only for stabling overnight when the carriage sidings at Monument Lane were full.

There were suggestions, not all of which were sensible. One gentleman wrote to the "Birmingham Post" just before closure, suggesting conversion of the line into a 'motor road'. The idea was humorously torpedoed by another correspondent a few days later:–

"What is the estimated volume of fast long-distance motor traffic from Monument Lane to Harborne? How wide a road is it proposed to construct in the space occupied by a single line of railway? What will city-bound traffic do when it reaches the junction with the Stour Valley line – dive into the canal? . . . It would be as well if (your correspondent) were to think for two minutes before rushing into print with fatuous suggestions as to the concrete application of his petrol-fume-dreams."

A more reasonable suggestion, via the pages of "Railway Magazine", was made in 1943. With wartime petrol rationing of unprecedented severity, and gross overcrowding on city bus services, the two writers proposed reopening of the Harborne line to passengers. They suggested a push-pull service at half-hourly intervals would be feasible, with tickets issued on board trains. Later in the year the correspondence was developed by Patrick B.Whitehouse, later a founder member of Birmingham Railway Museum at Tyseley. He too suggested the use of push-pull trains, and omission of the Monument Lane stop, which would make a fastest ever Harborne-New Street time of fifteen minutes practical. Management was fully occupied attempting to keep the wider railway on a war footing, so could spend no time or resources considering or developing ideas such as these, whatever their undoubted merits.

When working a push-pull set, the driver controlled the engine's regulator and brake from a specially equipped guards compartment at one end of the train while the fireman remained on the loco footplate at the other. Push-pulls had never been used on the branch. Their advantages on short or busy branch lines, eliminating time wasted while the loco ran round its train and/or used the turntable, were obvious. They were also governed by extra regulations and when the LNWR applied to use them on the branch in 1908 the Board of Trade would not sanction it. However, in June 1950 the Stephenson Locomotive Society ran a special to Harborne, the first passenger train over the branch for almost fourteen years. This was a push-pull set, and the accompanying photograph shows the sixty-year-old ex-LNWR Webb 2-4-2 tank engine (British Railways' number 46757) ready to depart from Harborne, red lamp on its buffer beam, most definitely in 'push' mode. There were to be a few more specials before the line closed completely in 1963 . . .

The Harborne branch had a twig of its own, just south of Rotton Park Road station, which served Mitchells & Butlers Brewery at Cape Hill. Only half a mile long, it was operated by the brewery's pint-sized locomotive, "John Barleycorn", seen here outside its shed on 12th July 1947. It was replaced in 1951 by a less diminutive engine which was imaginatively named "John Barleycorn II". *(Don Powell collection)*

[Diary : Notes : Closely Observed Trains]

Bomb damage to Snow Hill, Platform 1, 10th April 1941.

(courtesy of Birmingham Post & Mail)

Diary

1940

September 28th - Lifford station closed.

September 30th - Canley Halt opened.

November 14th-15th - Coventry blitz, cathedral and much of city centre destroyed, station damaged.

November 19th-20th - Bomb damage to Birmingham's New Street and Snow Hill stations.

1941

January 27th - Closure of stations on Camp Hill Line as wartime economy.

April 8th-9th - Air raid caused severe damage to Birmingham Snow Hill, especially to the down side, where much of the roof was destroyed.

April 10th - Further bomb damage to New Street station. Damage to the tunnels between New Street and Five Ways closed the West Suburban line for eight days.

May 5th - Closure of Soho Road, Handsworth Wood and Wood Green (Old Bescot) stations.

November 10th - Compulsory brake-testing stop in down trains at Blackwell abolished.

1942

WD and S160 heavy freight locos first appeared in Britain.

1944

October 2nd - Five Ways station closed - closure confirmed 1950 - new station opened 1978.

1945

May 7th - End of the war in Europe. Newton Road station closed.

October 1st - Express passenger service restored by GWR, Snow Hill-Bristol.

December 31st - First new post-war restaurant cars appeared on 11.45am Snow Hill-Paddington express and 6.10pm return service.

1946

First "County" Class locos built by GWR.

Repairs carried out to Snow Hill and glass replaced in the roof.

1947

First 2-6-0 (4F) 'Flying Pigs' built by LMS.

Severe winter weather during January, February and March, causing disruption to rail services across the country. One of the most exposed lines in the area, between Walsall and Rugeley, was only cleared by three Super Ds working behind the snowplough!

December - Last "Princess" Pacific completed by LMS named "Sir William A.Stanier FRS.". The nameplate now has pride of place in the foyer of Stanier House, Birmingham.

First British main line diesel loco, No.10000, completed by LMS.

Removal of overall roof on the LNWR side of New Street virtually completed by the end of the year.

LMS and GWR became part of British Railways at midnight on December 31st.

Notes

Perhaps the first word associated with World War Two bomb damage in the West Midlands is 'Coventry'. The air raid of 14th November 1940 claimed over 500 lives and destroyed the cathedral, along with most of the city centre. The railway station, where much needed rebuilding of the London bound platform had begun in 1939, was also damaged. At least 40 high explosive bombs fell on the lines near the city, preventing any traffic moving in or out. At first, the only available route for trains between Birmingham New Street and London was via Hinckley and the Midland main line to St.Pancras! Despite this, the lines linking Coventry with Birmingham and Leamington re-opened on a very limited basis just two days after the raid, and all lines out of the city returned to what passed for normal by the end of the month.

The fiftieth air raid on Birmingham, the worst up to that point, occurred on the night of November 19th-20th 1940, killing over 1,500 people. Both main line stations were hit. At Snow Hill, most of the glass was blown out of the booking hall roof and the clock was damaged. The only casualties were some booking clerks in the ticket office, who were cut by flying glass. The dining room of the former hotel, which was also hit, had earlier been used as an emergency casualty station for injured servicemen returning from Dunkirk. Further raids in the spring of 1941 caused more serious damage to Snow Hill. Three high explosive bombs hit the station on the night of April 8th-9th, one badly damaging the down island platform, together with the steel columns supporting the roof above it. A second bomb exploded in the fish dock beneath the station and a third penetrated the steel decking carrying track near Platform 11 (up side relief line) and exploded in the parcels yard. A pair of women's knickers was blown up into the girders above Platform 5, alongside a pair of airman's trousers. They fluttered happily in the breeze together for several weeks afterwards.

New Street station suffered on several occasions, a fact recalled in a feature article published in the "Birmingham Mail", on 1st November 1957. A Mr.Ted Taylor described how he had been in charge of rail traffic control in the station area, directing operations as best as he could from "a disused tunnel once used for the transit of heating apparatus to the various platforms". Given the circumstances, this 'nerve centre' was slightly more resistant to bomb damage than most other places in the vicinity. The first bomb hit the station on the night of 15th-16th October 1940, falling near No.5 Signalbox and injuring three people. In a later raid No.1 Signalbox, at the Euston end of the station, was virtually demolished, but the signalman escaped with nothing more than shock, although a colleague in No.2 box was killed by schrapnel in a later raid. On the night of the big raid, 19th-20th November 1940, Ted Taylor was on duty in his 'tunnel' when, at about 1.30am, he was thrown off his seat as a bomb demolished the "Malt Shovel", the nearest pub to the station. It was situated at the end of Queen's Drive and was very popular with off-duty station staff, being known as the "porters' pub". After the 'all clear', Ted emerged to find two small children wandering around in a daze. They lived in Aston and had come into a shelter at the station because they thought it was safer and quieter than their home area. There were no train movements into or out of New Street for two days following this raid. One bomb thought to have hit the station and exploded during the raid, was found eighteen months later, with its fuse still intact!

On 10th April 1941 the station was bombed once more and the damage inflicted on the tunnels between New Street and Five Ways, caused the West Suburban line to be closed completely for eight days. Perhaps the most frightening personal experience suffered by Ted Taylor occurred as the train from Walsall in which he was travelling entered New Street just as the station was being bombed:-

"I was in that train with an assistant traffic controller. We threw ourselves on the floor of the carriage as the glass and debris came hurtling down. When we got out of the train we learned that the parcels office had been hit as well as the cloakroom on Platform 1 - but by some miracle no one was killed that night".

E.A.Cowper's magnificent roof, although grimy and unkempt since the 1920s, had spanned the LNWR side of the station for almost a century. It was damaged and severely shaken during the air raids and after the war it was found to be unsafe, so it was dismantled during 1947.

A catalogue of damage to the railways in the region would make a long and depressing list; a very few examples must suffice. Among the numerous strategic targets was the Austin factory at Longbridge. It was learnt after the war that German pilots navigating with the aid of the railway lines, relied on maps which still showed Cofton Tunnel. The Old Park, the Wednesbury works of Metro-Cammell, was one of many Black Country factories that were damaged. On 1st January 1941 a bomb meant for Cadbury's and/or the railway fell on the canal bridge next to Bournville station, blasting a hole through it and causing the water to pour out into Bournville Lane. On 26th February in the same year the goods station at Lawley Street, which had been damaged by fire before the war, had much of its roof removed in a raid. In one raid on the yards at Washwood Heath, an incendiary bomb landed on the top of one of the gas holders, causing panic and consternation, until a Saltley engineman raced up the holder's external stairway and threw it off! A house at Pikes Pool, alongside the Lickey Incline, suffered a direct hit, killing everyone inside. It happened as a freight train was passing and the stationmaster at Blackwell, who was also an air raid warden, thought that sparks from the two hard working bankers may have alerted the pilot. The train was undamaged.

Stations were closed as wartime economy measures - Lifford in 1940, all local stations on the Camp Hill and Soho Loop lines in 1941 and Five Ways in 1944. These closures were confirmed as permanent after the war. Canley Halt, a mile west of Coventry, opened on Monday 30th September 1940. It lay a short walk from the Standard Motor works and other important factories, all of which were engaged in war work. The station relieved the pressure on some of the hard-pressed workmen's bus services.

Most passenger services were reduced in number and in speed during the war and the 1944 LMS time-table showing the Birmingham-London services, by both routes, illustrates how badly they were affected. Before the end of 1942, some ex-Midland 4-4-0 Compounds, almost forty years old, were pressed into service on the Euston-New Street expresses, due to a shortage of any better alternatives. It was reckoned that, if these locos were well maintained, they could keep to the wartime schedules with up to 11 coaches on. As the war progressed holiday trains were few and those that did run were packed. On-board refreshments all but disappeared.

Existing locomotives were not maintained to peacetime standards, they had - like the government's hard-pressed housewife Mrs.Sew & Sew - to 'make do and mend'. New locomotives had to be built, as cheaply as possible, to cater for the increase in all types of freight traffic and to ease pressure on those already in service. A further 250 of Stanier's 8F 2-8-0s were built, some for overseas work, while at the end of 1942, the Ministry of Supply placed orders with British loco firms, for a new 2-8-0. This was the "Austerity" heavy freight loco, designed by Robert A.Riddles and classified WD (War Department). 935 were eventually built. When new their appearance was

	WEEK DAYS									
	a.m.	a.m.	a.m.	a.m.	a.m.	a.m.	a.m.	a.m.	p.m.	p.m.
London (Euston) ....dep.	6 20				9 45					2 25
" (Paddington) ...... "		8 40	9 10			10A25		1130		
Birmingham (New St.)..arr.		1120				1B22				2 10
" (Snow Hill) "	11 9		1146		1 20		1 40		2 5	5 2
Wolverhampton (H.L.).. "		1151				2 28		2 44		4 43
" (L.L.).. "	11S40		1211		2 7				5 8	6 6

	WEEK DAYS—Continued									
	p.m	p.m	p.m	p.m	p.m	p.m	p.m	p.m	ngt.	ngt.
London (Euston) ....dep.	4 5	4 25	6 0	6 10	7 5	7 40	9 35	1155	12 p0	12 n0
" (Paddington) ...... "										
Birmingham (New St.)...arr.		6 59		8 24	1021		1240		3 14	
" (Snow Hill) "	6 41				8 55	1128			3 52	3 59
Wolverhampton (H.L.).. "		7 50		9 8						
" (L.L.).. "	7 9				9 23	1135		3 50	4 32	4 35

	SUNDAYS									
	a.m	a.m	p.m	p.m	p.m	p.m	p.m	p.m	p.m	ngt
London (Euston) ....dep	1010	1110		4 15		7 5		8 50	1155	
" (Paddington) ...... "			4 0		6 10		8 10			12 0
Birmingham (New St.)...arr.		2 6		7 11		1025		1211	2 52	
" (Snow Hill). "	1 42		7 40		8 52		1152			3 52
Wolverhampton (H.L.). "		2 46		7 45		11 6		a.m 1220	3 42	
" (L.L.)... "	2 12		8 30		9 19					4 32

Extract from the LMS time-table for May 1944, showing the service between Birmingham and London by both routes.

(courtesy of Robert Pearson)

something of a shock. A description in the "Railway Magazine" (Jan/Feb 1943) ran:-

"The external lines of the new type are of a distinctly 'free lance' description ...the stumpy stovepipe chimney, and the barrel with its larger diameter than that of the smokebox are both unusual, as is also the profile of the cab; and the tender has no resemblance to anything previously turned out for British use."

Easily capable of hauling 1,000 tons of freight, the WDs were soon contributing handsomely to the war effort. They continued in use for many years afterwards, as captured by Michael Mensing's lens at Acocks Green in 1961. If the WDs looked odd, their appearance was as nothing compared to the S160 Class 2-8-0s, supplied to the US Army by three of the principal America builders - Alco, Baldwin and Lima - and imported for use in Britain from December 1942. 174 of these engines were loaned to the Great Western and some were shedded at Wolverhampton (Stafford Road and Oxley) and Tyseley. From September 1944 they were all handed back for use in Europe as the Allies advanced. Some S160s are still at work in eastern Europe, particularly Poland; one is working on the Keighley & Worth Valley Railway and the parts of another are currently waiting assembly at Birmingham Railway Museum.

The twenty Great Western twin railcars, ordered in 1938, were all built and put to work relieving overcrowding, especially on the Birmingham-Cardiff run. During the first part of the war that service had been suspended, then reinstated with just one diesel railcar per day, at 9.10am from Snow Hill and 4.45pm from Cardiff. It was supplemented by a basic steam service in each direction, with extra stops at Stratford and Hall Green, but overcrowding was still acute. To alleviate this problem the twin cars employed on this route from the end of 1941 had a standard GWR 10-compartment corridor coach inserted between them as a trailer, transforming the twins into triplets and raising the seating accommodation to 184.

The LMS continued to build diesel shunting locos during the war years, for economy of use in its largest yards, including Bescot. They weighed 55 tons, had an excellent power/size ratio with a tractive effort of 34,940lbs., could work an unbroken eighteen hour shift, required only one man on the 'footplate' and carried sufficient fuel for a week. The large driving cab was supplied with a small cooker, complete with frying pan and toaster. A series parallel switch on the control panel increased the tractive effort by almost 50%, which was useful for working with a very heavy train, on a steep gradient, or for adopting a very slow crawler speed when the loco was used on permanent way work.

Two of the new designs which appeared immediately after the war quickly became familiar sights in the region. H.G.Ivatt's 2-6-0 4F freight locos first appeared on the LMS in 1947. They were powerful and strong, but poor steamers, and a nightmare for firemen. This fault was corrected after nationalisation when the double chimneys were replaced by singles and the draught modified. Their most obvious characteristic was an extreme ugliness, with a very high running plate. This was for ease of maintenance, but it left all their guts permanently exposed. They were known as "Flying Pigs".

In contrast, the Great Western's CME, F.W.Hawksworth, produced the new "County" Class of express loco in 1945. This was the last design of a long line that had begun with Churchward's "Saints" of 1902. Hawksworth employed and improved upon the best features of similar locos, especially the modified "Halls". The superheating of the boiler was more efficient thanks to the increased number of small tubes, and the very high boiler pressure of 280lb./sq." was equalled only by the Southern's "West Country" Class. In appearance the tender was different from earlier types and there was a continuous splasher above the locomotive driving wheels, topped by a straight nameplate. These locos soon found employment on Paddington-Snow Hill-Birkenhead trains. Unfortunately, no "County" escaped the cutter's torch.

90268 with an unfitted freight on the northbound slow line at Acocks Green on 8th May 1961. Over seven hundred of these 2-8-0 heavy goods engines were built during the Second World War. They were employed over virtually the whole of the British railway system and were classified as WD (War Department). Without them, the rest of the country's stock of locomotives would have been in an even more run-down condition in 1945. The signal stands alongside the goods loop, whose own signal – worked in conjunction with the catchpoints in the foreground – is almost hidden behind a very substantial telegraph pole.

(Michael Mensing)

Wartime alien at Worcester – a member of the S160 Class built in America for the US Army and loaned to the GWR during 1943 and the first part of 1944.

(Jim Peden collection)

The 9.20am from Birkenhead Woodside to Bournemouth West eases into the sunlight and shadow of Birmingham Snow Hill on 17th June 1957. The locomotive is 1022 "County of Northampton", the Great Western's final express passenger type. There were thirty members of the class, designed by F.W.Hawksworth. 1000 "County of Middlesex" appeared in 1945, the only one to be built with a double chimney. Working boiler pressure was 280 pounds per square inch, very high for the time. Unlike other Great Western named types, a continuous splasher over the driving wheels was topped by a straight nameplate. The boiler was based on that for Stanier's 8F 2-8-0 heavy freight loco of 1935, some of which were built at Swindon during the war. Sadly, not a single "County" escaped the scrapyard. The light engine, 0-6-0T No.9614, is waiting bunker first for a path through the tunnel. *(Michael Mensing)*

Closely Observed Trains
(Memories of those who were there, 1919-1947)

Joe Waltier had a long career on the railway, beginning in 1919 and ending in the 1960s. All of it was spent based at Ryecroft shed, Walsall, where he began as a cleaner, at the age of fourteen. When he started, his hours were 6am-5.30pm Monday to Friday, finishing at 1pm on Saturday. As he was then smaller than anyone else at Ryecroft he was the only one able to get inside the side tanks of a Webb tank engine, turn round inside the tank and remove any obstructions from the feed. Others found this work much more awkward, being unable to turn round. The obstructions were coal or slack, because the bunker was very near the tank intake, which would be buried by a full load of coal. It was as well to take on water before the coal. At least Webb's patent steam injector, only used on LNW locos, had a reversible jet and this sometimes helped to clear obstructions.

As a cleaner Joe often worked with the joint maker as a fitter's mate. They sealed the column joints for the safety valves with black lead, and the dome joints with asbestos. These often needed attention to curb minor leaks, especially the column joints and, as Joe remarked, *"nobody knew about the dangers of asbestos in those days"*. In the course of time, Joe became a fireman, then a driver.

As a fireman he quickly gained a route knowledge of all the ex-LNWR lines around the West Midlands also working on the 'Camdens', the fitted freights to London. Soon he was allowed to fire on longer journeys, including the excursions to Blackpool. At this time (around 1930) Joe recalled that these trains consisted of old non-corridor stock, with a stop to use the toilets at Crewe.

On one occasion, the train was also divided at Crewe, and a moment's carelessness returning from the toilets resulted in a couple Joe knew having enforced separate days out, the husband at Blackpool and the wife at Llandudno! The Blackpool trip was no holiday for the fireman, a hard road with a lot of firing to do, *"you were too tired to enjoy yourself, you had a job to pick your arms up sometimes, and it would feel as though you'd just emptied the tender"*.

A few older drivers could be harsh to a young fireman, but Joe was lucky and most were considerate - Alf Sankey was a name remembered over the years, *"a real gentleman, almost like a father to me"*. Joe fired trains on the Harborne line, where the turntable was only long enough for a tank engine. Any other engine had to travel tender first in one direction, and it was always harder to see beyond the rectangular bulk of the tender than the rounded boiler of the loco. His driver at the time, Charlie Reeves, was once turning a tank engine on the table at Monument Lane shed, which was overlooked by the windows of the manager's office, when the manager leaned out and enquired why he needed to do it, Charlie replied, *"You can walk forwards and you can walk backwards, but you know which is the easiest, don't you?"*

After Joe became a driver, qualifying by spending a day 'passing out' under the watchful eye of Inspector Lucas, he soon discovered that one of the most difficult lines to work was the Leighswood Siding, which was a short branch off the Walsall-Lichfield line at Pelsall, serving collieries and brickworks. The curves and gradients were so severe that a bridge over the canal was approached by a short sharp gradient of 1:28, which fell away to 1:33 on the other side! One real hazard, on account of the sudden changes in the gradient, was the danger of 'dropping the plug'. This was a safety device designed to prevent damage to the firebox. It consisted of a lead plug in the roof of the firebox, which was also the floor of the boiler. If the boiler water ceased to cover it, even briefly, the heat from the firebox would melt the lead. This would minimise the risk of a boiler explosion but the loco would lose all power and the hapless driver risked instant dismissal. It was as well to have as full a boiler as possible on the Leighswood branch otherwise, if the water was low, it could slop about on the gradients and expose the plug.

An incident with plugs early in his career was vividly remembered by Joe. The Dudley Dasher motor train, which provided the shuttle service between Dudley and Dudley Port, was allocated to Ryecroft shed but based at Dudley. As a young cleaner aged 15, he sometimes had to catch the last passenger train of the day and spend much of the night at Dudley shed preparing the 'dasher' for its crew. He always worked completely alone and in the dark, save for the dim light of a gas lamp. On one occasion he noticed that the water in the boiler was so low that none was showing on the gauge. No matter, thought Joe, he could light the fire, unscrew the washout plug on the face of the firebox and supply water to the boiler with the hosepipe, as he usually did. In this instance however, the washout plug proved to be highly resistant to the spanner and it would not budge. There was a real danger of the other plug - the lead one - melting, causing a sudden end to Joe's brief career on the railway. Fortunately, after what seemed like hours, the washout plug yielded and the hosepipe could do its work, *the minute I could see water showing in the gauge glass, I was happy again*".

During the Second World War there was a shortage of firemen at Ryecroft, so Joe fired more than he drove, although on several occasions he drove ambulance trains between the south coast ports and the Midlands. His railway career continued after the war and he retired, from Ryecroft, in the 1960s. His last work involved instructing other drivers how to drive the first generation diesel multiple units, the only motive power at the shed after it closed to steam in June 1958.

Frank Ash started as a train reporter at Walsall, aged 17, in 1932. He booked trains in and out, received reports of any delays from the guards and sent a daily report sheet to the control office in Birmingham. At the age of 20 he became a porter at Bescot, before moving to Darlaston. It was here that he became interested in signalling as a career and he found that all three signalmen who worked the adjacent box, Darlaston Junction, were willing to help him. After finishing his afternoon shift as a porter, at 10.30pm, he would often go to the box and help work it until 5am, before returning home to sleep. In this way he learnt all the rules and regulations and the bell codes, as well as gaining valuable 'hands on' experience, because this was a busy box at night, with all the freight traffic emerging from Bescot yard. He successfully applied for a vacancy as a porter/signalman - at Darlaston Junction! As soon as he arrived on his first day his colleagues in the adjacent boxes - Darlaston Green and Willenhall - sounded the six-bell emergency code. Only after he had dashed frantically about outside, putting detonators on the tracks, did they ring him to announce the 'all clear'.

Life in a signalbox could be very lonely, except for the occasional visiting driver whose train had been brought to a stand at the signals. Each signalman knew most of his colleagues only as voices on the phone; they could pass each other in the street and be none the wiser. Frank Ash came to work boxes at Darlaston Junction, Darlaston Green, Wednesfield Heath (on the Grand Junction line which passes north of Wolverhampton High Level, busy with freight at night) and Essington, north of Bloxwich. When new to that box he once 'gave the road' to a freight train, which had half an hour to clear the junction at Ryecroft before the next passenger train was due. The Bloxwich signalman was furious because, as he explained, the passenger train would be delayed. That particular freight driver was notorious for ambling along very slowly, so that he would be entitled to overtime payment. The only exception was on a Friday, when he drove too quickly in order to get home and out to the pub. Revenge was sweet one Friday soon afterwards, as Frank put him into the goods loop and kept him there for some time.

One awkward incident at Essington involved the 'Salop' freight from Shrewsbury to Bescot, and the last passenger train of the day from Birmingham to Rugeley. The Salop divided at Essington and the front portion drew forward before backing into the sidings to pick up some wagons. At this point there was a 'click' in the box, showing that the track circuit from Hednesford was occupied. No further train was approaching from the north but the rear part of the Salop was rolling back towards Hednesford. The trap points were activated so as to halt its progress, although this would probably result in a lineside pile-up. The passenger train was held at the box and the Salop loco was sent north to investigate. Frank issued its driver with a Wrong Line Order, as demanded by the regulations. The rear of the train was found to have stopped short of the trap points and after almost an hour the loco returned to report that all was well - minus the Wrong Line Order, which the driver had incorrectly given to the Hednesford signalman. In doing this, he had effectively closed the line! However, passengers in the Rugeley train were becoming increasingly restless, so Frank sent it north, which was strictly against the rules. When its loco returned from Rugeley as a light engine, its driver collected the Order from Hednesford and dropped it off to Frank. Three days later a visiting inspector congratulated Frank on the way he had handled the incident - but he knew only half the story!

Only once was Frank ever reprimanded. Working Bescot No.4 box he was supervising 60 wagons over the hump, sorting them into various sidings. It was the end of his shift and he was busy talking to his colleague who had come to relieve him. In a moment of distraction he pulled the wrong point lever. He realised this immediately because the whole frame shuddered. He had tried to change the points which were at that moment under the locomotive but, by a stroke of luck, the point blades were between the engine wheels and the tender wheels, so damage was minimal.

During the war, although still enjoying his work, the hours were very long and Frank decided to search for better prospects elsewhere. He had a driving licence and, when a friend urgently needed a lorry load of goods delivering to Coventry he paid Frank the same amount as the regular driver would have received. This was better by far than his pay as a signalman, so he changed jobs soon afterwards, but always looks back on his days on the railway with affection.

Two wartime events brought about a remarkable upsurge in interest in railways. In the spring of 1943 the son of the curate at St.Nicholas' Parish Church, King's Norton, was confined to bed with measles at the family home in Westhill Road. To cheer Christopher up his father, Rev.Wilbert Awdry, invented a tale about Edward, the first in what was to become the Thomas the Tank Engine series, which soon began to delight younger children all over the country.

In 1942 Ian Allan was nineteen years old, unable to play an active part in the war due to the loss of a leg in an accident four years earlier. He worked in the publicity department at Waterloo station, which received many enquiries from members of the public about the Southern Railway's locomotives. This prompted

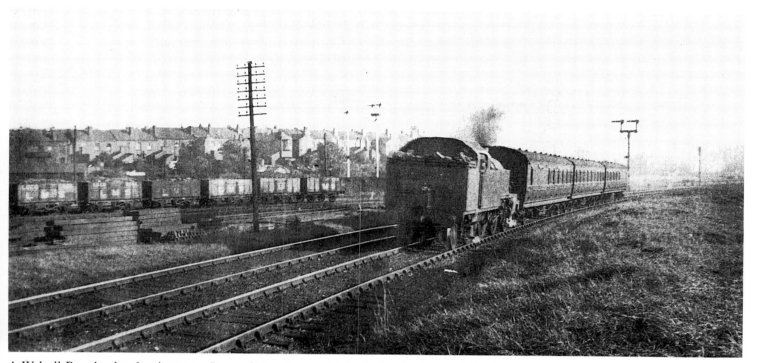

A Walsall-Rugeley local train passes Ryecroft Junction, 1934, in the hands of one of Fowler's 2-6-2 tank engines of 1930. The wagons are full of loco coal for the shed.

(Frank Ash)

him to compile and publish the "ABC of Southern Locomotives", which consisted of lists of the locos in service, together with specifications for each class and type, plus some photographs - an invaluable reference for anyone who observed trains. Costing just one shilling (5p) it was within range of most boys' pocket money, and fulfilled a long-felt need. Boys could now record the locos they had seen, generally by underlining their numbers, and compare notes with their like-minded friends. Ian Allan soon produced similar books for the GWR, LMS and LNER. Not surprisingly these pocket-sized books were an overnight best-seller even though in many countries, in the middle of the worst war in history, information about railways in this form would be deemed as highly sensitive, their publication banned and their publisher viewed with suspicion - or worse.

Earlier in the war the "Railway Magazine" had cautioned its readers to act sensibly in pursuit of their interest, reminding them of restrictions on photography, as troops assembling at stations, railways connected with defence, or bomb damage to any railway were all subjects forbidden to the amateur photographer. In a paragraph entitled "The Appearance of Evil - A Warning to Railway Enthusiasts" (July 1940) it further cautioned that, *"Train-timing is a practice unknown to the majority of ordinary travellers, and the careful noting of gradient changes and landmarks such as signalboxes and bridges may be - and in our experience has been - regarded by the suspicious as preparation for a plan of sabotage. Should the train-timer find anyone viewing him with suspicion when making notes, the best course is to explain quite openly what is being done and to desist for the time being if it appears that suspicions are still being harboured. ...... the avoidance by transport enthusiasts of the appearance of evil should be regarded not merely as a duty towards the preservation of the good name of their hobby, but also a small contribution to the national wellbeing."*

In theory at least, enthusiasts in the Birmingham area could sample the usual delights of New Street and Snow Hill stations but, for obvious reasons, these places had few attractions for the casual visitor before the return of peace. For those who lived to the north of the city, or who wanted to see trains speeding along a busy main line, the Trent Valley was the place to be - Rugeley, Lichfield or Tamworth. From the war years until the end of steam clusters of boys could be seen at these locations, the numbers sometimes swollen to well over a hundred during the summer holidays. And it was almost invariably boys, with hardly a girl to be seen. In today's much changed society the formerly rigid division between the hobbies, interests and perceived abilities of the sexes is less distinct. For example, more women and girls attend football matches than ever before, women have proved themselves to be excellent mountaineers - and they also drive trains and work signalboxes in increasing numbers, in the Birmingham area as elsewhere on the network. If steam still held sway along the Trent Valley it is probable that the balance of the sexes enjoying the spectacle would be less one-sided than it once was.

It was at Tamworth, during 1944, that the growing hobby received a setback. Boys gathered there were no longer content simply to watch the trains; many of them had taken to trespassing and putting pennies on the tracks to have them flattened by the trains. They were then retrieved as 'trophies' to show to their mates back at school. Following a police raid on the site, several Birmingham lads appeared in court in November and, although their cases were dismissed, the growing hobby received unwelcome publicity. This incident prompted Ian Allan to found the "ABC Locospotters' Club". For just one shilling (5p) prospective members received a badge, notebook and pencil, a discount voucher valid for any Ian Allan book and a lifetime's membership card for the club. Most importantly, each member had to sign a pledge not to trespass on railway property. Anyone breaking this pledge would be instantly expelled from the club. Like the books, the club was highly successful and, as the 'respectable face of the hobby', was soon granted access for organised visits to engine sheds and locomotive workshops all over the country.

Memories of a happy and well-spent youth for some boys who may now be grandfathers! This was Tamworth on Saturday 26th October 1946, as a local for Rugby departs. The problem of litter has always been with us, it would seem, although short trousers have become part of history.

(courtesy of Birmingham Post & Mail)

George Green was a pupil at Rugeley Grammar School and between 1942 and 1944 he travelled by train from his home in Hednesford. It was usual for both his daily trains to be in the charge of one of Fowler's 2-6-2 tank engines of 1930. His observations confirmed the general view that these locos were poor steamers, "and if ever No.2 appeared there would be a stop at Brindley Heath to raise steam, even with three coaches". The journeys soon developed George's interest in all aspects of the railway, an interest which had begun in 1938 when, aged ten, he had 'wangled' some illegal footplate rides aboard Super Ds on the Cannock mineral lines. However, for some obscure reason, Trent Valley station was out of bounds to grammar school boys, and woe betide anyone unfortunate enough to be spotted by the part-time woodwork master as he alighted from the train. (Mr.Pegler travelled from Stafford on three days per week.)

Weekends and school holidays were different, and George soon found himself spending Saturday mornings, and then whole days, down at 'the Trent', out by the 9.37 from Hednesford and back home by the 6.34pm. Station staff, aware of his deep interest, allowed him to stay on the platform, whereas the lads arriving off a later train, the 9.45am ex-New Street, were directed by station foreman George Morgan to a lineside field, on the down side, south of the station. The 9.45am ex-New Street in fact worked from Crewe to Crewe, via Wolverhampton, New Street, Walsall and Rugeley - a useful running-in turn for an engine which had just been overhauled at the works, and a good train for the lads to travel in, conveniently timed, always with a good chance of exotic motive power.

Despite the passage of more than half a century, George Green remembers the loco which hauled his train on the first Saturday he went to Trent Valley - un-named "Patriot" No.5549, working tender first. Local services from Birmingham were often in the hands of Fowler 2-6-2 tanks, some of which were based at Ryecroft, Aston, Monument Lane and Bushbury. The later 2-6-4 tanks (4P/Stanier/1935) were far superior, with a number at Aston and Monument Lane. One engine which regularly handled the sparse local service along the Trent Valley line was "Prince of Wales" 4-6-0 of 1911, No.25673 "Queen of the Belgians", confirmed by a colour slide in the author's possession, which depicts it at Lichfield in 1948 although, sadly, the quality is not good enough to justify reproduction. Unlike today, Rugeley T.V. was not merely a local station. One main line service which called there, around 10.11am, was the 6.40am through service from Euston to Windermere, invariably packed to bursting point during the summer months.

After leaving school in 1944, George Green spent a year at Walsall Commercial College, commuting by bus, which fostered an interest in Walsall Corporation's unique and very varied fleet. Most afternoons were free and some were - inevitably - spent at Trent Valley. The journey from home by bus *"necessitated something like a 20 minute walk to Trent Valley and many were the times that signals for all four lines were seen to be in the 'off' position long before the station was reached and it was always a question of how many of the four trains had passed by the time one set foot on the platform. Freight traffic was, of course, extremely heavy, everything from local trip workings to train*

A good view of a "Patriot" taken from an unusual angle through the open window of Lichfield Trent Valley signal box, complete with signalman's sooty bell. Besides coal in the tender there are two sets of fire irons, tank air vents (amongst the coal), the open tank filler hatch – with hinged lid, plus the pick-up syphon bowl dome. The loco was 5503 "The Leicestershire Regiment", but this was early in the BR era, 21st July 1952, so what you see is 45503 "The Royal Leicestershire Regiment". *(Roger Shenton)*

loads of tanks or other weapons of war."

A few years later, now working in the divisional offices at Derby, George was able to solve a cold weather problem for travellers on one Saturdays only train. The 10.50am from Wolverhampton to Walsall and Rugeley returned from Rugeley at about 2.30pm. Normal motive power was an ex-Midland 4-4-0 2P, unloved by train crews but still useful on locals and as pilots to heavy expresses. Such an engine was too long for Rugeley's 42 foot turntable, so the outward trip would be tender first and without the benefit of steam heating for the passengers, as these locos had no steam pipe at the front end. Three of the much newer Ivatt Class 2 2-6-0s of 1946 were shedded at Derby, where their talents were being wasted as mere station pilots. They had steam pipe fitments at both ends, and a quick role reversal with the 4-4-0s solved the problem, ensuring that, from henceforth, passengers were nicely warmed.

Roger Shenton was a schoolboy during the war, living in Lichfield and drawn, like many of his friends, to observe the workings of the railway at the Trent Valley station. The best place to be was the pathway off the Old Burton Road, adjacent to the northbound platform. As well as all the usual activity on the main line, and on the high level line above, the scene was enlived, during 1943 and the first part of 1944, by the arrival of troop trains packed with American GIs. They were encamped on the golf course around Whittington Barracks, prior to their departure for the D Day landings. The triangular section of land sandwiched between the Old Burton Road and the High Level line - still vacant today - was utilized to marshal the troops conveyed by road to and from the barracks. At a time of severe rationing (most younger children had never tasted sweets or chocolate, or seen a banana), the trains were not the only attraction, as the GIs generally gave the lads gifts of gum, sweets, chocolates, magazines - cigars and cigarettes, these last to be passed on to their parents........naturally!

After 1945 it was not, of course, possible to repatriate all prisoners of war immediately. Some remained for two years and more, others settled here permanently by choice. Before returning home, they were found some work and a place to live. For example, the displaced persons camp at Streethay, near the station, housed Italian former prisoners of war who were formed into a permanent way gang, under the formidable command of Ganger Charlie Bannister, who himself fought in Italy and could converse with the Italians. He lived in one of the fog cottages at Armitage.

As a regular visitor to Trent Valley, Roger was able to see something of the devastation caused by the accident of 1st January 1946. Twenty people were killed, making it one of the worst railway accidents ever to occur in the West Midlands. The 6.08pm local train from Stafford to Nuneaton was standing at the up platform, with brakes fully on, when it was struck from the rear by the Fleetwood to London Broad Street fish train. The local train's engine, "Prince of Wales" No.25802 was pushed forward 280 feet by the force of the impact. Three of its four elderly wooden coaches were destroyed, the other badly damaged. Roger recalls, a few days afterwards, seeing the loco on the sand drag, where it had come to rest, and the smashed remains of the ex-LNWR coaches stacked along the embankment opposite, clear of the collision site. In the subsequent enquiry the likely cause of the tragedy was found to be the weather. Signals and points seemed correctly set, to allow the fish train to run through on the fast line, overtaking the local as it normally did. However, it was later discovered that some frozen ballast had expanded, impeding the full action of the facing points. They were still set for the platform road although the signalman (the box was 200 yards away) was able to operate the point lever and thought they had been reset for the main line. With the points apparently set correctly, he was, of course, able to set the signals for that course too. The driver of the fish train, flung across his

A later member of Stanier's 5MT 'Black Five' Class, built at Crewe in 1947, was No.4758. These were some of the most successful and efficient mixed traffic locomotives ever built. This one, complete with BR number, is seen passing the original Lichfield Trent Valley station buildings with the afternoon express fitted freight from Camden to Glasgow on 23rd August 1952. It was withdrawn at the end of steam on British Rail in 1968.
(Roger Shenton)

cab when the loco hit the points, was unable to do anything to prevent the collision. The Inspector, Colonel Woodhouse, recommended that point rodding this far removed from a box should have proper 'guiding' to remove the potential for excess movement and to ensure that it operated correctly.

Near the end of the 1940s Lichfield Trent Valley was a hive of activity, with about forty people working in or around the station.. The booking and parcels office, open from 6am until 9pm, was run by two clerks. Tickets issued included a 3rd class single fare to Euston for just 19/11d - one old penny short of £1. Three shunters each worked eight-hour shifts, and their cabin can still be seen next to the Burton Road overbridge. The main line signalbox needed six people, a signalman and boy on each of three eight-hour shifts. Signalman Ted Brazier was strict but fair, teaching his three sons the rudiments of his art in the box, also 'training' Roger and his friends, so long as they took his instruction seriously and didn't think it was just a bit of fun. Signalmen in many boxes all over the country indulged in this strictly illicit but essentially harmless activity, adding to the enjoyment and enthusiasm of those many lads who were interested, some of whom would later have a career on the railway, often because seeds such as this were sown at an impressionable age.

Lichfield Trent Valley also boasted a taxi rank, a splendid garden on the up main line platform (which later blossomed spectacularly in Coronation Year, 1953) and a buffet, which was run by the senior porter's daughter until it closed about 1947. Outgoing parcels included products from Bound Brook Bearings, who sent daily consignments of ball bearings all over the country by passenger train. Roger observed, after beginning work at the station in 1949, that one of their main customers seemed to be the Hoover Factory on the Great Western Road at Perivale, a splendid Art Deco building now sadly demolished. The first up local passenger train each day, the 5.44am from Stafford, always brought large quantities of parcels traffic for the shops in

Lichfield, especially Woolworths, with boxed fresh fish for Malarkey's, opposite the Regal Cinema. These parcels called for 'all hands' to convey them across the main line barrow crossing and into the hydraulically operated lift up to the high level platform, from whence they would be taken on the short rail journey to Lichfield City and then by van to their final destinations. Other incoming freight was destined for the Ministry of Food depot, the South Staffordshire Waterworks and Evans' Maltings. There was the usual supply of house coal. Cattle and horses were taken to the cattle dock behind the down platform, the remains of which still exist. Most of these animals came from Ireland via Holyhead, and the vet had to be called whenever some were injured or badly fatigued.

Unlike many of his companions, Roger had the foresight, on occasion, to take his box Brownie camera with him. Happily his pictures survive, and some are reproduced here as an authentic glimpse of the closely observed trains that were a feature of life in those now distant days.

For those who experienced the immediate post-war years, thoughts of rail travel at the time are punctuated by memories of the numbers of people still in the armed forces, gross overcrowding and the appalling winter of 1947.

G.T.Pugh was doing his National Service with the R.A.F. just after the war, based at Kidlington, Oxfordshire. One particular journey is still fresh in his mind. Returning from a weekend's leave, he joined his usual Sunday evening train at Wolverhampton Low Level. It should have enabled him to be back in camp before midnight:-

"The train was fairly full at Wolverhampton, but when it arrived at Snow Hill the platform was just packed with servicemen. They all managed to pile on and it was now near bursting point, with men standing in all the corridors. Nearing Fenny Compton, the train began to slow down, and finally drew up at the platform. As this was not a scheduled stop we began to

Possibly one of the ugliest locomotive designs ever, the 'Flying Pig'. This was 2-6-0 mixed traffic loco (4MT) No.43023, built at Horwich in 1949 to an LMS design of 1947 by H. G. Ivatt. It is seen at Lichfield Trent Valley on 19th March 1949 with a special shuttle service to Tamworth, provided when NE/SW services due to stop at Tamworth were diverted through engineering works via Lichfield T.V.High Level. This loco was withdrawn in 1967. Although ugly, these locos were easy to maintain as most moving parts were easy to reach and the cab was large, affording good protection from the weather. *(Roger Shenton)*

suspect that something was wrong and sure enough a railwayman came to announce that a bearing on one of our carriage wheels had seized up, and that our carriage would have to be taken out of service. As there was no replacement, we should have to try our luck and try to squeeze into the other already overcrowded carriages. I frankly thought it impossible, but we pushed and struggled and finally managed it. I ended up being pushed and pulled through one of the compartment's sliding windows.

We arrived at the camp after 23.59 hours and duly ended up on a charge the next day. Our commanding officer, who was not noted for his sense of humour, made the comment that we should have caught an earlier train, and duly awarded us all seven days confined to barracks."

John Lilburn joined the Austin Motor Company at Longbridge as an electrical engineer in September 1946. The arrival of winter, the following January, caught the country at a low ebb. Food rationing was almost as harsh as in the worst days of the war, most basic commodities were in short supply and there was a fuel crisis. The bad weather made distribution of coal very difficult and there were long and frequent power cuts for both industrial and domestic users. The 'Austin' generated much of its own power and it had adequate coal stocks, so although it could have continued production without interruption, the company was not allowed to do so whilst other less fortunate industries had to close down, as this would have been seen as not fair' in the political climate of the day.

In March the long winter gave way to a damp spring, followed by a fine summer. Holidaymakers could not then travel to the Costa Brava, and the delights of traffic jams on the M6 formed part of an undiscovered future. Rail was the only option for long distance travellers, which brought its own set of problems to John and his friends:-

"In August 1947 I went with three friends on an overnight train from New Street to Glasgow. This was during the Birmingham holiday fortnight and the platform was solid with would-be passengers. We decided that the only way in which we were going to get seats together, or indeed seats at all, was for the smallest member of the party to get in through a window and "reserve" seats for us all! This was done and we had a table and four seats all the way to Glasgow. There was an accident somewhere in Scotland and a very long detour was made, resulting in our arrival in Glasgow being about six hours late. Such was rail travel at that time."

Bernard Lazenby served in the R.A.F. during the war, after which he signed on for three more years. He was based at Wellesbourne Aerodrome, near Stratford-upon-Avon, where pupil pilots in the Army Glider Regiment were trained. When the snow and gales arrived this airfield, unlike most others in the region, did not close 'for the duration' and send its personnel home. Many of the 1,500 people based here were put to work, trying pointlessly and unsuccessfully to keep the runway open, using only shovels and brushes!

A weekend in March saw Bernard in London, where his fiancée, Vicki, was working at the Daily Mail Ideal Homes Exhibition at Earl's Court. It coincided with the sudden thaw, with accompanying floods and gales, ensuring that the journey from Paddington back to base was anything but routine. Long sections of track were flooded and speed was reduced to a crawl - "sleepers and at times the rails were under water. The driver was well blessed with guts to have carried on."

The train had left London at 8pm on the Sunday evening but did not arrive at Leamington until 1.15am, 3 1/4 hours late, by which time the only member of staff on duty was a ticket collector, very unhappy at having been kept waiting for so long. He informed the party of about fifteen weary servicemen that there was no transport back to camp as the roads were blocked with fallen trees and no accommodation left in town as servicemen arriving on earlier trains had filled it all. No, they could not use the waiting room to sleep in, but they could try the coaches of the Stratford train, stabled in the bay platform, and

The last section of E.A.Cowper's war-damaged roof awaits removal at New Street, as girders for the temporary platform canopies rise underneath it, 31st December 1947. *(courtesy of Birmingham Central Library)*

with that he locked up and left. Bernard spent a cold and virtually sleepless night in a first class compartment, with only the sound of the howling wind for company and a grit-filled carpet off the floor as a blanket. He was turfed out by a carriage cleaner before 6am and went to join a 100-strong queue of servicemen waiting for a nearby transport cafe to open at 7.

"We eventually had a cuppa standing on the pavement, the front of the queue had eaten all the food! The sun now shone - no wind. The streets looked blitzed - slates, tiles, branches, glass - it had been a wild night."

Back at the railway station, R.A.F.Wellesbourne had sent a message for any personnel attempting to return. The roads were blocked by fallen trees and debris, but "we should follow the road to camp to assist those at work with saws and axes to cut forward to meet those doing the same task from the opposite end." Instead, Bernard and a colleague decided to make the most of the first hint of warmth and sunshine for many weeks by spending a few leisurely hours in Jephson Gardens writing to their fiancees. The Stratford line was cleared of trees by the afternoon and they caught the first train along it at about 4pm. "At Stratford a taxi driver told us he could get to the drome with a small detour. The amount of trees down and sawn through convinces me of the worst gales in my 50 odd years in this vicinity". At the camp, a late meal in the Sergeants' Mess was followed by the luxury of a shower and a warm bed. The next day saw many hours of uninterrupted sunshine, finally convincing Bernard that his nightmare journey - and the epic winter - were both at an end.

And so too was the idea that railways could, or should, be run effectively as private companies. The Labour Government elected with a large majority in 1945, was committed to public ownership of all the utilities and major industries. The railways which had played such a vital role during the war, were struggling to recover.

The Roman god Janus, after whom January is named, has two faces, one looking to the past, the other to the future. As nationalisation approached, effective from 1st January 1948, the LMS unconsciously showed two faces here in the Midlands. The bomb-damaged roof over the former LNWR platforms at Birmingham New Street was gradually removed and the work was all but completed by the date of the accompanying photograph, 31st December 1947. Earlier in the same month the first main line diesel-electric loco to run on a British railway was completed at Derby, painted jet black, numbered 10000 and with the stainless steel initials 'LMS' riveted to the sides. It was soon hauling expresses along the Trent Valley, more of a novelty then to the boys gathered at Tamworth, Lichfield and Rugeley, than main line steam is to today's generation.

The new era brought new problems and new opportunities but the fact that the railways passed from private to public ownership did nothing to affect the hard working commitment to the job that has always been a major strength of those working in the industry. Since 1948 the pace of change on the railways, now once again in private ownership, has accelerated in the Birmingham area, as elsewhere, but that - as they say - is another story.

The LMS's first and only main line diesel locomotive. This 1600hp machine, with Co-Co wheel arrangement and English Electric engines, was built at Derby, entering service in December 1947. No.10000 also had the metal letters 'LMS' riveted to the sides as an unsuccessful deterrent to removal by British Railways. It is seen here, in its black livery with silver stripe, passing Lichfield Trent Valley with the 10.10am Blackpool Central to London Euston on 6th July 1952. On withdrawal in 1963 the loco was purchased as scrap by Cashmore's of Great Bridge.

(Roger Shenton)

ACKNOWLEDGEMENTS

Many people have readily offered help, advice, assistance, use of facilities, photographs, etc. in the preparation of this book. Particular thanks are due to the following –

Frank Ash	– memories	Robert Pearson	– archive material
Anna Burke	– Birmingham Post librarian	Don Powell	– signalling information
		G.T.Pugh	– memories
George Green	– memories	Jane Rogers	– GEC Alstholm, Metro-Cammell
Bernard Lazenby	– memories		
John Lilburn	– memories	Roger Shenton	– memories
Simon Mole	– Railtrack, Birmingham	Dave Spencer	– archive information
Maurice Newman	– railwayman	Ken Werrett	– proof reading
Dan Pawson	– archive material	Joe Waltier	– railwayman

Some of the above provided photographs, as did the following – Frank Brown, Chris Banks, Roger Carpenter, Alex Chatwin, Robert Darlaston, W.E.Hall, L.Hanson, Michael Mensing, Jim Peden, F.W.Shuttleworth.

The author wishes to state that although he received much valuable assistance from railway staff and others working in an official capacity, any unattributable opinions expressed in the text of this book are entirely his own.

BIBLIOGRAPHY

"THE BIRMINGHAM TO LEICESTER LINE"
Chris Banks
1994 : Oxford Publishing Company
ISBN 0 86093 465 9

"BLACK COUNTRY RAILWAYS"
Ned Williams
1995 : Alan Sutton Publishing
ISBN 0 7509 0934 X

"BY RAIL TO HALESOWEN"
Michael Hale and Ned Williams (joint authors and publishers), 1974

"AN HISTORICAL SURVEY OF SELECTED GREAT WESTERN STATIONS"
Volume Two, R.H.Clarke, 1979   ISBN 0 86093 0 15 7
Volume Four, C.R.Potts, 1985   ISBN 0 86093 1919
Oxford Publishing Co.

"AN HISTORICAL SURVEY OF SELECTED LMS STATIONS"
Volume One, Preston Hendry & Powell Hendry, 1982
ISBN 0 86093 168 4
Oxford Publishing Co.

"A HISTORY OF THE GREAT WESTERN RAILWAY"
Volume Two 1863-1922 E.T.MacDermot, revised C.R.Clinker
1964 : ISBN 0 7110 0412 9
Volume Three 1923-1947 O.S.Nock
1967 : ISBN 0 7110 0304 1
Ian Allan

"A HISTORY OF THE LMS"
Volume Three, 1939-1948 O.S.Nock
1983 : Allen & Unwin
ISBN 0 04 385097 9

"THE HISTORY OF THE LONDON & NORTH WESTERN RAILWAY"
Wilfred L.Steel : 1914

"LMS 150"
Patrick Whitehouse & David St.John Thomas
1987 : David & Charles
ISBN 0 86288 071 8

"THE MIDLAND RAILWAY"
Roy Williams 1988 : David & Charles
ISBN 0 7153 8750 2

"OVER THE LICKEY"
Donald Smith & Derek Harrison
1990 : Peter Watts Publishing
ISBN 0 906025 71 0

"A REGIONAL HISTORY OF THE RAILWAYS OF GREAT BRITAIN"
Volume 7, The West Midlands   Rex Christiansen
1973 (and 1991) : David & Charles
ISBN 0 7153 6093 0

"THE RAILWAY TO WOMBOURN"
Ned Williams, 1986 Uralia Press
ISBN 0 9511223 2 0

"RAILWAYS OF THE WEST MIDLANDS, A CHRONOLOGY 1808-1954"
Ed.Charles R.Clinker : 1954
The Stephenson Locomotive Society

"SALUTE TO SNOW HILL"
Derek Harrison 1978 : Barbryn Press
ISBN 0 906 160 006

Various journals, newspapers and documents, all acknowledged within the text, especially the *"Railway Magazine"*, published continuously since 1897.

STATION GAZETTEER

Includes name of station, opening and closure dates to passenger traffic, other names, etc. Two sets of dates indicate opening, closure and re-opening (eg; Stourbridge Town), sometimes followed by final closure (eg: Princes End). Where no closure date is given, the station has been continuously open to passengers on the same or similar site.

ACOCKS GREEN 1852 (renamed 'Acocks Green & South Yardley' in 1878, now 'Acocks Green' again)

ADDERLEY PARK 1860

ALBION 1853-1960

ALDRIDGE 1879-1965

ALVECHURCH 1859

ASTON 1854

BAPTIST END 1905-1964

BARNT GREEN 1840

BERKSWELL 1844 (opened as Docker's Lane, renamed Berkswell 1853, Berkswell & Balsall Common 1882, now reverted to Berkswell.)

BESCOT 1847

BILSTON CENTRAL 1854-1972 ('Central' added in 1950)

BILSTON WEST 1854-1962 ('West' added in 1950)

BIRCHILLS 1858-1916

BIRMINGHAM MOOR ST. 1909-1987 (replaced by present stn. in 1987)

BIRMINGHAM NEW ST. 1851 (temporary stn. for local service to Wolverhampton) 1854 (main stn.)

BIRMINGHAM SNOW HILL 1852-1972 : 1987 ('Snow Hill' not added until 1858)

BLACKWELL 1840-1965

BLAKEDOWN 1852 (formerly CHURCHILL, then CHURCHILL & BLAKEDOWN)

BLAKE ST. 1884

BLOWERS GREEN 1878-1962 (named 'Dudley (South Side) & Netherton before 1921)

BLOXWICH 1858-1965 (new stn.to the north, 1989)

BORDESLEY 1855

BOURNVILLE 1876 (earlier known as STIRCHLEY ST. and STIRCHLEY ST.& BOURNVILLE)

BRADLEY & MOXLEY 1862-1915 (site near today's Bradley Lane Metro stop)

BRETTELL LANE 1852-1962

BRIERLEY HILL 1858-1962

BRIGHTON ROAD 1875-1941

BRINDLEY HEATH 1939-1959

BROCKMOOR HALT 1925-1932

BROMFORD BRIDGE 1896-1965 (racecourse stn., served only by specials)

BROMLEY HALT 1925-1932

BROMSGROVE 1840

BROWNHILLS (Midland) 1884-1930

BROWNHILLS (LNWR) 1849-1965

BUSHBURY 1852-1912

CAMP HILL 1841-1941

CANLEY 1940

CANNOCK 1859-1965 (new stn.1989)

CASTLE BROMWICH 1842-1968

CHESTER ROAD 1863

CHURCH ROAD 1876-1925

COLESHILL 1839-1916 (see also Forge Mills)

COMPTON HALT 1925-1932

COOMBES HOLLOWAY HALT 1905-1927

COSELEY 1902 (replaced Deepfields, opened 1852, 400 metres to north)

COUNDON ROAD 1850-1965

COVENTRY 1838

CRADLEY HEATH 1863

CUTNALL GREEN HALT 1928-1965

DAISY BANK 1854-1916 : 1919-1962

DANZEY 1908 (opened as Danzey for Tanworth)

DARBY END 1905-1964

DARLASTON 1837-1965 (known by various combinations of the words 'Darlaston' and 'James Bridge' until 1913, when the name was fixed by request of Darlaston Urban District Council)

DROITWICH 1852 (known as Droitwich Spa since 1923)

DUDLEY 1850-1964

DUDLEY PORT (Stour Valley platforms) 1852

DUDLEY PORT (South Staffordshire Line platforms) 1850-1964

DUNSTALL PARK 1896-1916 : 1919-1968

EARLSWOOD LAKES 1908 (now known as Earlswood)

ERDINGTON 1862

ETTINGSHALL ROAD 1852-1964

FIVE WAYS 1885-1944 : 1978

FOLESHILL 1850-1965

FORGE MILLS 1842-1965 (renamed COLESHILL in 1923)

FOUR OAKS 1884

GORNAL HALT 1925-1932

GRAVELLY HILL 1862

GREAT BARR 1862 (now named HAMSTEAD)

GREAT BRIDGE (NORTH) 1850-1964 ('North' added 1950)

GREAT BRIDGE (SOUTH) 1866-1915 : 1920-1964 ('South' added 1950)

GREAT WYRLEY 1858-1965 (also known as Wyrley & Cheslyn Hay)

GRIMES HILL & WYTHALL 1908 (opened as Grimes Hill Platform, now named WYTHALL)

HAGLEY opening date uncertain, first appeared in time-tables in 1862

HALESOWEN 1878-1927 (open until 1960 for workmen's trains)

HALL GREEN 1908

HAMMERWICH 1849-1965

HAMPTON-IN-ARDEN (LNWR) 1837 (stn.moved $1/4$ mile south-east to present site, 1884)

HAMPTON-IN-ARDEN (branch from Whitacre) 1839-1916

HANDSWORTH & SMETHWICK 1854-1972

HANDSWORTH WOOD 1896-1941

HARBORNE 1874-1934

HARTLEBURY 1852

HARTS HILL 1895-1916

HATTON 1852

HAZELWELL 1903-1941

HEATH TOWN 1872-1910

HEDNESFORD 1859-1965 : 1989

HENLEY-IN-ARDEN (branch terminus) 1894-1908

HENLEY-IN-ARDEN (North Warwickshire Line) 1908

HIMLEY 1925-1932

HOCKLEY 1854-1972 (site is west of the present Jewellery Quarter stn.)

HUNNINGTON 1883-1919 (stn.sidings served the Bluebird toffee factory)

ICKNIELD PORT ROAD 1874-1931

KENILWORTH 1844-1965

KIDDERMINSTER 1852

KINGSBURY 1839-1965

KINGS HEATH 1840-1941 (known as MOSELEY before 1867)

KINGS NORTON 1849

KNOWLE & DORRIDGE 1852 ('& Dorridge' added in 1899, now named just 'Dorridge')

LANDYWOOD 1908-1916 (new stn.1989)

LANGLEY GREEN 1885

LAPWORTH 1854 (known as KINGSWOOD until 1902)

LEA HALL 1939

LEAMINGTON SPA 1852 ('Spa' not added until 1913)

LEAMINGTON SPA AVENUE 1844-1965

LICHFIELD CITY 1849

LICHFIELD TRENT VALLEY 1847 (Trent Valley Line platforms):

1849-1956 ; 1988 (high level platforms)

LIFFORD 1885-1941 (third station)

LONGBRIDGE 1915-1960 (workmen's services only)

LYE 1863 (no station in Britain has a shorter name)

MARSTON GREEN 1844

MILVERTON 1844-1965 (opened as 'Leamington', underwent several name changes which included the words 'Warwick', 'Leamington' and 'Milverton' in various combinations)

MONMORE GREEN 1863-1916

MONUMENT LANE 1854-1958

MOSELEY 1867-1941

NEWTON ROAD 1837-1945 (near today's Tame Bridge Parkway stn.)

NORTHFIELD 1870

NORTH WALSALL 1872-1925

OCKER HILL 1864-1890 : 1895-1916

OLDBURY (main line) 1852 (replaced on same site by SANDWELL & DUDLEY in 1983)

OLDBURY (branch terminus) 1885-1916

OLD HILL 1866

OLD HILL HIGH ST. 1905-1964

OLTON 1869

PELSALL 1849-1965

PENN HALT 1925-1932

PENNS 1879-1965

PENSNETT HALT 1925-1932

PERRY BARR 1837 (the present station is on the same site as the Grand Junction Railway original)

PLECK 1881-1917 : 1924-1958

PRIESTFIELD 1854-1962 (Wolverhampton-Worcester line platforms): 1854-1972 (Wolverhampton-Birmingham line platforms) Stn.site on curve, just south of Monmore Green stop on the Metro.

PRINCES END 1863-1890 : 1895-1916

PRINCES END & COSELEY 1853-1962 ('& Coseley' added in 1936)

REDDITCH 1859 (current stn. is fourth; second stn. 1868-1974)

ROTTON PARK ROAD 1874-1934

ROUND OAK 1852-1962

ROWLEY REGIS 1867

RUBERY 1883-1919 (open for workmen's trains until 1964)

RUGELEY TRENT VALLEY 1847

RUGELEY TOWN 1870-1965 : 1997

RUSHALL 1849-1909

SALTLEY 1854-1968

SELLY OAK 1876

SHENSTONE 1884

SHIRLEY 1908

SHORT HEATH (Clark's Lane) 1872-1931

SMALL HEATH 1863 (opened as 'Small Heath & Sparkbrook')

SMETHWICK 1852 (now named Smethwick Rolfe St.)

SMETHWICK JUNCTION 1867-1996 (later known as Smethwick West)

SOLIHULL 1852

SOHO (LNWR) 1867-1949

SOHO (GWR) 1854-1972 (known as Soho & Winson Green from 1893)

SOHO ROAD 1889-1941

SOMERSET ROAD 1876-1930

SPON LANE 1852-1960

SPRING ROAD 1908 (opened as Spring Road Platform)

STECHFORD 1844 (replaced by stn. on present site in 1882 and renamed Stechford for Yardley)

STOKE WORKS 1852-1965

STOURBRIDGE JUNCTION 1852 (present station and junction, south of earlier, opened 1901)

STOURBRIDGE TOWN 1879-1915 : 1919

STREETLY 1879-1965

SUTTON COLDFIELD 1862

SUTTON PARK 1879-1965

SUTTON TOWN 1879-1924

SWAN VILLAGE 1854-1972

TETTENHALL 1925-1932

THE HAWTHORNS 1931 (Christmas Day) -1968, served only by football specials

THE LAKES 1935 (opened as The Lakes Halt)

TILE HILL 1864

TIPTON FIVE WAYS 1853-1962 ('Five Ways' added in 1950)

TIPTON OWEN ST. 1852 ('Owen St.' added in 1950)

TYSELEY 1906

VAUXHALL 1869 (also known as VAUXHALL & DUDDESTON, now known as DUDDESTON)

WALSALL 1847

WALSALL WOOD 1884-1930

WARWICK 1852

WATER ORTON 1842

WEDNESBURY CENTRAL 1854-1972 ('Central' added in 1950)

WEDNESBURY TOWN 1850-1964 ('Town' added in 1950)

WEDNESFIELD 1872-1931

WEST BROMWICH 1854-1972

WHITACRE 1842-1968 (stn. on junction site after 1864)

WHITLOCK'S END 1936 (opened as Whitlock's End Halt)

WIDNEY MANOR 1899

WILLENHALL 1837-1965

WILLENHALL STAFFORD ST. 1872-1931

WINDMILL END 1878-1964

WINSON GREEN 1876-1957

WITTON 1876

WOLVERHAMPTON HIGH LEVEL 1852 (known as plain 'Wolverhampton' 1852-1853 and since 1972; 'Wolverhampton Queen St.' 1853-1885 and 'Wolverhampton High Level' 1885-1972)

WOLVERHAMPTON LOW LEVEL 1854-1972 ('Low Level' added in 1856)

WOMBOURN 1925-1932

WOOD END 1908 (another Great Western 'Platform')

WOOD GREEN 1881-1941 (also known as Wood Green [Old Bescot])

WORCESTER SHRUB HILL 1850

WYLDE GREEN 1862

YARDLEY WOOD 1908 (opened as Yardley Wood Platform)